# DYING TO KNOW

# DYING

RUNNING THROUGH

# TO

A PANDEMIC

# KNOW

## ROB DONOVAN

Matador
Unit E2 Airfield Business Park,
Harrison Road, Market Harborough,
Leicestershire. LE16 7UL
Tel: 0116 279 2299
Email: books@troubador.co.uk
Web: www.troubador.co.uk/matador
Twitter: @matadorbooks


ISBN 978 1 8031 3011 8

British Library Cataloguing in Publication Data.
A catalogue record for this book is available from the British Library.

Printed and bound in the UK by TJ Books Limited, Padstow, Cornwall
Typeset in 11pt Minion Pro by Troubador Publishing Ltd, Leicester, UK

Matador is an imprint of Troubador Publishing Ltd

This work is dedicated to the memory of all those lives that have been lost in this global pandemic and especially to the more than 170,000 souls who have died prematurely in our land and to all those who mourn their passing.

# CONTENTS

# Preface

I am a runner with a special local circuit. One and three-quarter miles up to the top of the hill at Little Trevalgan, within the Penwith peninsula in Cornwall – and then back down again. 3.5 miles for the free flow of thoughts.

And this is my literary device. You, the reader, are my companion on a run that is a summation of all my runs during the coronavirus pandemic in 2020. You are privy to the thoughts that bubble up from my subconscious. What you read is, in part, autobiographical. You are also able, like me, to delve into the bole in my magic tree to access the fruits of research into matters that need further investigation. A touch of magical realism does not come amiss at the best of times – but these runs of mine are being completed in the worst of times. I am running in a pandemic. I need to know more about how the world has become gripped by a virus that is proving so deadly. Why are so many dying before their time? You share my journey of discovery over the months in this first year in the pandemic.

# 1

## POINTS OF VIEW

The turning point at Little Trevalgan always gives me pleasure. Even a little chuckle. It does not matter if the view of St Ives Bay is masked by mist or cloud; the knowing that it is downhill all the way home from now on sends waves of satisfaction through this body that I have been persuading to run gently upwards for the last twenty-five minutes. Twenty-five minutes up. Twenty minutes down. A bit of a Cornish hill. Of course, it used to take less time. Back in 2013, I was running the round trip in thirty-three minutes. But that was seven years ago, and a lot has happened since we first moved to Cornwall.

For starters, I am seventy-one now. But that has little to do with it. I know and admire a fellow runner, Robin, over in the east of England where we used to live, who is six years older than me and defying nature by now running even faster only a year after an unfortunate encounter with an automobile on a training run that left him in hospital with fractures of the femur, collarbone, and skull. The car was a write-off. I would love to match Robin for pace, but I cannot.

I am dying to reach the summit of the hill, and I know I still can if I just keep on moving forwards. Slowly, slowly, catchee monkey. Where did that saying come from? I love monitoring my thoughts when I am running. Especially when I am moving so slowly uphill. Plenty of time to let the stream of consciousness flow. I wrote parts of my last book on this very hill, finding the stride and pace to reach the turning point. My dad, probably. Or my wolf cub's handbook, my guide to another life. He served in India in the Royal Army Pay Corps before the last war when he became an officer in the Royal Artillery. He tried to catch a bit of action to make himself feel better. But he failed. So at least no killing to hide.

Not that I was ever a wolf cub for real. My mum was worried about the expense and whether my dad would mind. She worried a lot about what my dad would mind. Oh my! A shiver of delight. That was my first cuckoo of the year. I forget from one year to the next what thrills await on this mile and three quarters stretch. That sound is so divine. So strong. So grounded. Coook-koo. Coook-koo. I look to my left towards the open rolling moorland crowned with granite tors and two derelict chimney stacks. That bird has its being over there. Coook-koo. Coook-koo. They used to burn off the arsenic in those edifices. St Ives under the surface. That was one of the joys of first being here. Discovering the history of the Cornish mining industry and imagining the lives of those industrial toilers. Most died before their time. That was the price of the pay packet and the camaraderie. Can you – should you – find joy in learning about the premature dying of others?

A few metres from the turning point at Little Trevalgan

Above the ground, there are such wide vistas here. Birdsong is so voluminous if you let it be. I look to my right and glance down at the bluebells and red campions, then over the yellow gorse and white cow parsley, across the fields to where the sheep are grazing. I can hear a chaffinch – such a busy and pure sound, full of optimism – and that must be a song thrush, blessed with melody. I passed John coming the other way last week on one of these runs. He is a walker in his eighties, a lovely man of God who used to be chief mining surveyor at South Crofty, the last mine to close Camborne way. A temporary mining captain, too. My living link to life under the ground. His daughter and her husband are our neighbours. 'Good to see you, John!'

'Good to see you, Rob!' And I continued running on, downhill, elated.

John and his friend Jim came over for coffee and a chat back in those early days after our arrival. Jim passed away three or four years ago, now, but that was in part the strain of looking after his wife, who had developed dementia. Jim was a big man in every way and if John was tin, Jim was water. Most of Jim's water seemed to be underground, too. Jim had risen from plumbing to the top of South West Water. Jim and John could tell a tale or two.

Birds sing, but this tale of theirs sighs. There once was a young miner they knew well. Everyone liked him. He had spirit. Tea break was approaching. Deep down the mine shaft, on the spur of the moment, he decided to arrive early. Quick as a flash, prompted by who knows what, he grabbed onto a passing kibble, a large bucket rising slowly up the mine shaft to the surface. He miscalculated. He was left hanging on by his fingertips. The men at the top of the shaft saw him coming into view as the bucket neared the surface. His last words were: 'I can't hang on anymore. Goodbye.' It took the other half of the day to get his body back to the surface.

Cornish tin miners, photographed by J.C. Burrows in 1894

Death comes in many forms. On the run before this, I passed a dog walker whom I knew. 'How are you?' My greeting.

'OK.' A pause. 'So far.' Her reply.

Provisional certainty is a philosopher's delight, but in this context we both knew what she meant.

We are, you see, living in a time of pestilence.

Now, there is a thought. I am running in a time of plague as tens of thousands die in this country – the United Kingdom, aka Britain – which has recognised me as a citizen since birth. In fact, Britain gave me the status of a subject when I was born in 1948. Nearly everyone with a close connection to the United Kingdom was called a "British subject" back then. The British Nationality Act, 1948, redefined a British subject as any citizen of the United Kingdom, its colonies or other Commonwealth countries. That meant that between 1949 and 1983, a Commonwealth citizen was synonymous with being a British subject. But then, immigration became an issue and we were on a long and winding road that has led to Brexit. Since 1983, in the words of the GOV.UK official online statement, "very few people have qualified as British subjects".

Subject or citizen? United Kingdom or Britain? Does it matter? It does to me. I am a republican and I am no one's subject. I am a citizen. Citizen Rob. More self-aware than the seventies TV comedy figure of "Citizen Smith", I hope. But very much focused on the socialist ideal and certainly with no time for the institution of monarchy, which by its very survival and popularity weaves patterns of deference into our hard-won democracy. No one is my better nor I their subject, by simple accident of birth. No way.

How a country treats its citizens has always been a big deal for me. For starters, my country – which comes down to my government – should never act as if it has some natural right to determine my destiny and that of others, against our declared wishes or against our best interests. Not in a democracy. Imperfect a system it may be, but democracy is the best form of government for ordinary people. It is the fruit of our struggle to rein in the selfishness and greed of the rich and powerful.

I love these timeless moments when a thought takes over and I transcend the tiredness and ageing of this body and lose myself in the stream of consciousness that bubbles up from the depths of my inner being. My soul. My subconscious. I feel the lightness of the guardian angels that sit on each shoulder of my essence. They once took over my life and soaked up all memory of a woodshed episode until I was ready to absorb the experiences myself and reintegrate them into my being. I confess I have borrowed them from Islamic theology, these guardian angels. I used to teach Islam to school students but that is a story for another time.

In Islamic tradition, a guardian angel is an angel who looks after every being in life, sleep, death or resurrection. Each person is assigned four *Hafaza* (guardian) angels, two of which keep watch during the day and two during the night. Muhammad is reported to have said that every man has ten guardian angels; perhaps he believed that, too. I am curious, though, why he would have felt we needed so many. Two at a time should be enough; we are not under that much threat.

I am, you see, a glass that's more than half-full kind of person. My Christian vision resonates with that audacious Hebrew affirmation from Genesis 1: *God said, 'Let us make man in our own image' and the goodness of creation was transformed. God saw that the making of men and women had rendered creation so good that it was now 'Very good'.* What a hymn to hope! I am with Alexander Pope, who, around three hundred years ago, coined a line that still sounds well today: "Hope springs eternal in the human breast".

Hope will get us through this time of pestilence. I breathe more easily as I steal a glance upwards to the back of the sign that has just come into view at the top of the hill. I know I should run with my head up, but sometimes it feels too hard, too daunting. I prefer to run blind and give way to whatever comes into my mind. I submit to my subconscious and my angels. Live in the moment. That is my running mantra. Each leaden pace forwards has its five-beat rhythm:

Live – in – the – mo – ment.
Live – in – the – mo – ment.
Live – in – the – mo – ment.

And this is when my historical side kicks in. My running saga will gift me these magic interludes for a more detailed sharing with you, my companion, such episodes as touch my being whilst I am running. Think of it like climbing a tree, with new worlds glimpsed as you move higher and higher, from branch to branch, and you disappear into the trunk for the next adventure.

Samuel Pepys kept his diary from 1660 to 1669 and so provides us with a first-hand witness account of the Great Plague of London in 1665. He had hope and lived to tell the tale. In fact, he was part of the moneyed elite who did not live in cramped and insanitary conditions and so was much less at risk. In his annual summary at the end of 1665, he wrote, *I have never lived so merrily (besides that I never got so much) as I have done this plague time*. There are always likely to be some winners at a time of disaster.

Nonetheless, Pepys was concerned about the pestilence. On 16th August, he wrote:

> *But, Lord! How sad a sight it is to see the streets empty of people, and very few upon the 'Change'* [the Royal Exchange]. *Jealous of every door that one sees shut up, lest it should be the plague; and about us two shops in three, if not more, generally shut up.*

Pepys was evidently alert to the economic consequences of the plague, rather like a Tory neoliberal backbencher today.

Daniel Defoe was a five-year-old who survived that London plague. His novel *A Journal of the Plague Year* was first published in 1722 when he was in his sixties. Wonderfully, he seems to have used the personal account of his uncle, Henry Foe, who had lived through the 1665 plague, keeping a journal to record this eruption of death into the London landscape and his life. Daniel, his nephew, had the wit and wisdom to turn his uncle's diary into a novel, claiming it as a work of the imagination and then supplementing it with data about the plague that could have only come from hindsight.

Here, from the Defoe family, is the reality of living within a bubble of disease:

> *London might well be said to be all in tears... the shrieks of women and children at the windows and doors of their houses, where their dearest relations*

*were perhaps dying, or just dead, were so frequent to be heard as we passed the streets, that it was enough to pierce the stoutest of hearts in the world to hear them. Tears and lamentations were seen almost in every house, especially in the first part of the visitation; for towards the latter end men's hearts were hardened and death was always before their eyes, that they did not so much concern themselves from the loss of their friends, expecting that themselves should be summoned the next hour.*

How long, I wonder, before compassion fatigue takes over in our COVID-19 times?

Pepys and Defoe had an eye for the big stuff in history, those times of life and death that bring us face to face with the meaning of our very existence. They wrote as survivors, their works a testimony to the totality of such disease, the grimness of death, the power of hope and our capacity to overcome, albeit through a filter of self-interest.

Similar themes to those of Pepys and Defoe emerge in the work of the Colombian writer and Nobel laureate, Gabriel García Márquez, through the magical realism of his novel: *Love in the Time of Cholera* (1985). In Márquez's work, a key theme is that living in a time of pestilence is like dying; all that is familiar wilts and falls away. He shares with Alfred Hitchcock, the film director, a writer's joy in playing with reality. Hitchcock defended the improbability of some of his scenes with the line: *I distrust logic when it does not serve my purpose.* Marquez's justification for embracing magic in his writing is one I love, too. Those with developed western outlooks, he said, have forgotten an important truth: 'Reality isn't limited to the price of tomatoes and eggs.' Tell that to the Tory neoliberals!

We are in this for the long haul. Very few realise yet but read the runes. The old world dies, and in the new world we have no option other than to keep going. There may be no limits to this new way of living. The bubble of disease has settled on us and clicked tight. We need to understand, and we need hope. It is good that hope is a quality embedded within us as humans. Life in the bubble will have some cheer.

I am on the toughest stretch now. Once, over all these eight years of running up this hill, my body took over and said *enough*. I stopped running at this point. I must have been ill. What to reflect on to ease my passage to the summit? Let it be this. There must be a time for this at some point. Or perhaps not.

# 2

---

## MAGIC INTERLUDES
## AND COVID

When did I become aware the world had turned upside down and we were living through a time of plague? I should explain that I do not just write books; I also write blogs. My first blog post to focus on our pestilence is dated 10th March 2020.

Goodness, such a coincidence! A twist of fate. A matter of life and death. Thoughts of death and dying do bubble up in all of us from time to time. More so at times such as these. Dear Will, our Stratford word merchant, had the soothsayer proclaim to Caesar with shrill tongue: "Beware the ides of March". Only in my case, the warning should have been: "Beware 10th March". It was forty-six years ago, on that day in 1974, that my first wife wrapped our Ford Cortina round a lamppost on the A412 in Slough and died. They pulled me from the passenger seat, and three days later I emerged from my coma. Best not drink and drive. There! It is out. My woodshed episode.

We must keep going in this bubble of disease, this time of plague. I kept going all those years ago. Decided to opt for hope and lived to tell the tale. Death, I found, had lost its sting. My fear of dying faded almost clear away. My guardian angels, coating my memory, served me well.

That blog post on 10th March directly asked the question: "How far are we subject to deception?". I had had my eyes opened by a news story a day earlier about an eminent professor who explained on the radio that this new virus – COVID-19 – was essentially an airborne disease that was spread by coughs and sneezes. Yet we were all being advised to wash our hands, as if that would stop the viral infection. As the professor said, this advice might lead to fewer upset tummies but do little to stop the advance of the coronavirus.

I smelt the aroma of bullshit from there on in. The stench grew stronger and stronger as the days of March passed. All the time, we were hearing the same message:

> "We are acting on expert advice. We are following what our scientists and our medical authorities are telling us is the best path."

Politicians are the ones who have been invested with the authority to make decisions, not advisors. That fact was buried. And as the weeks passed, it became clearer and clearer that a swathe of scientists did not share the views of those in their community who were now prepared to collude with the leaders of government.

I could scarcely believe the story that was taking shape in my blog posts. This government – led by Boris Johnson and shaped by Dominic Cummings, the special advisor with a penchant for eugenics, this body of neoliberal Tories that I had tried so hard to prevent being elected only a few months ago – was daring to place the power of the purse and the pursuit of profits before the lives of people.

Heh! What if some percentage of some millions perish between now and whenever – we are building up "herd immunity" against the virus. In response, I wrote:

*We are being misgoverned by moronic buffoons following a malignant agenda.*

In mid-March, these barbarians did nothing to stop a quarter of a million people assembling over four days at the Cheltenham festival of horseracing and, in that same week, they allowed three thousand Spanish fans to fly in, untested, for a football match in Liverpool. Herd immunity in action. Denied, of course.

"Herd immunity? You cannot be serious. That is not our policy."

But it was.

Sometimes on my run, I pass roadkill. The black and white of a magpie or the creamy whiteness of a herring gull catch the eye as I skirt a crushed and dry-bloodied corpse. A beautiful flight cut short, not quite fast enough to escape the spin of wheels on blind automobiles. Those are the images forming now as I urge my body forwards to this summit. In 10 Downing Street, the wheels of power are primed for road-killing on an industrial scale.

I cannot rid myself of the horror of all that I now know about this pandemic.

I have kept my ear to the ground; I have read the real

news in online platforms such as *The SKWAWKBOX*. I know much more than most do. The public is there to be nudged and manipulated into acquiescence, its ignorance kept and further conserved. Mainstream media in March and April and most of May uttered little criticism of what Johnson and his lackeys were doing and not doing.

Of course, this malaise of misgovernment goes deeper still and back in time. It started with Cameron and Osborne and Duncan-Smith, and all their cronies, who gained power in 2010 and began to reshape Britain on neoliberal lines through their privatisation and austerity programmes as they strove to reduce government expenditure and cut back the size of the state.

When I am running down this hill of mine – and that is a joy that lies ahead – I get a panoramic view of the field that is now largely hidden from me as I force myself upwards. On that descent, I can look left and over the hedge and see this wide expanse where sheep graze from time to time. In the centre, and stretching down the slope, is a wide circle of granite rocks that have defied the ploughman for the best part of three thousand years. There are five or so large stones, the length of a grown man and twice as wide, and at least twenty smaller slabs. Survivors of a way of living crushed by the force of time. Men, women, and children lived out their lives across there, oblivious to the impermanence of their own actions and dreams.

Most of us here in Britain are as ignorant of the future as those guys were three millennia ago. The world I grew up in and recognise as my own – the world created by the post-WWII Labour government led by Clement Attlee – is now at a critical survival moment. That hard-won world which prized ideas such as fairness and equality and decency,

Running downhill, looking over the hedge towards
the field with the remains of an ancient settlement

whatever its own inconsistencies and malaise, is on the point
of suffering a similar oblivion. The new kids on the block will
be – and are – barbarians by comparison, believe me.

My wife of forty-four years, Louise, left a comment:

*Does our idiot of a prime minister realise that he could
get COVID-19?*

At that point, it seems not. But he did become infected a few
weeks later. All the bigwigs are showing solidarity with the
dead and dying – Johnson, Cummings, Hancock, Charles
Windsor and more – they have all, it seems, succumbed to
the virus. None of them, though, are dead.

Dead – dead – dead.

Dread – dread – dread.

That seems a fine chant to help my leaden legs continue
in motion.

But not very cheerful.

Perhaps I am not only living in fear of being infected. Maybe I also have some form of post-traumatic stress disorder (PTSD). I clocked up twenty-nine days of canvassing for Paul Farmer, the Labour candidate, in the general election in December last year. I did so with every expectation he would win. When the result was declared, the other guy – the Tory – had a majority of 8,700. I would have wept if I had not been so shocked.

None of this would be happening if Jeremy Corbyn had become the prime minister in 10 Downing Street. He is my kind of man.

A socialist fit for the 21st century.

Kind.

Compassionate.

Genuine.

Concerned.

And the leader of the Labour Party. At least, he was.

Another thought. Did you wonder who or what is behind *The SKWAWKBOX*?

Me too.

It is run by Steven Walker, who has close links to Jeremy and his allies in the Labour Party and the union, Unite.

Steven believes informed people are hard to exploit.

He quotes, with approval, George Orwell:

"In times of universal deceit, telling the truth is a revolutionary act."

Steven Walker is my kind of guy, too.

It is useful being able to reach into the bole of my magical tree like this. My mind can run freer even as my legs suffer.

When I was a student in '68, I marched with a mass of others through the centre of London chanting:

'Hey, hey, LBJ. How many kids have you killed today?'

Fifty-two years later, I am running up this hill and crying out, alone and free as a bird:

'Hey, hey, Boris J! How many guys have you killed today?'

The summit is almost in sight. Time, I think, to reference my first book: *The Road to Corbyn* (2016). A secular fantasy of a pilgrimage through the social and political landscape of the UK from 2010 to 2015, exposing deceit and self-deception. My attempt to understand why there was so much suffering in our country. John Bunyan's story of *The Pilgrim's Progress*, written over three hundred years earlier, had been my inspiration. My anger had found literary form. I was laying bare the right-wing mindset that forms to protect the interests of privileged wealth and power.

Our current malaise has such deep roots. On Wednesday, 29 January, England's chief medical officer, Professor Chris Whitty, declared that the UK was well prepared for the coronavirus outbreak. That was not true.

In October 2016, Exercise Cygnus had taken place. All major government departments, the NHS, and local authorities across Britain were involved. The capacity of the UK to respond to a pandemic was being tested and evaluated.

The findings of Exercise Cygnus have still yet to be published.

I must count my strides now to see myself through this stretch.

One – two,

De – ceit.

Three – four,

What – a – feat!

Five – six,

What – a – lark!

Seven – eight,

Left – in – the – dark.

Cygnus had revealed significant gaps in the NHS's "surge capacity". These gaps included a shortage of intensive care unit (ICU) beds and personal protective equipment (PPE). All of this, the result of a neoliberal Tory agenda for the privatisation of the NHS.

The mainstream media held back on this Cygnus story until 28th March 2020, when it appeared in *The Telegraph*. By then, the nation had been in lockdown for five days.

When I posted a blog, just before Johnson's screeching U-turn into a national lockdown on Monday, 23 March, Louise left this comment:

> *I have a long list of things I would not trust Johnson to do… all due to his lack of integrity, ability to make and keep commitments and promises… the cats who prowl the lane behind my house have a stronger moral compass than Johnson. How did we end up with this buffoon in No.10?*

I imagine Johnson and Cummings, cross-dressed as witches from Macbeth and bent double over their cauldron, spitting out magic spells and incantations as they conjure up their herd immunity potion.

"This is our virus to infect the masses!
This is ours to suppress and release!
This is ours to turn on and off!
Oh, but just check there are enough coffins!"

I am striving harder and harder to make sense of the surge of this pandemic racing towards me and everyone else. I am the researcher. I need to share my findings with you. That is my duty.

I know now that on Monday, 3 February, the Scientific Pandemic Influenza Group on Modelling (SPI-M) met. This was a key sub-committee of the Scientific Advisory Group on Emergencies (SAGE). Professor Graham Medley, the chair of SPI-M and a member of SAGE, was becoming increasingly fearful of the menace posed by the new virus.

Yet the prime minister, that same day, gave a celebratory speech at Greenwich, to mark the UK's departure from Europe, in which he talked about "a risk that new diseases such as Coronavirus will trigger a panic and a desire for market segregation that go beyond what is medically rational to the point of doing real and unnecessary economic damage".

He continued: "…at that moment humanity needs some government somewhere that is willing at least to make the case powerfully for freedom of exchange".

The UK under his leadership, he promised, will be that country "ready to take off its Clark Kent spectacles and leap into the phone booth and emerge with its cloak flowing as the supercharged champion".

You are members of the jury. Consider the evidence I have laid before you. The accused, by his own admission, prioritised his belief in neoliberal economics over the dangers posed by a new virus that had already prompted China to lockdown millions.

Is this man mad or bad or sad?

Or perhaps a combination of all three?

A week later, on Monday, 10 February, the UK Health Secretary, Matt Hancock, declared the virus a "serious and imminent threat to public health". The World Health Organisation (WHO) named the virus: COVID-19.

From Saturday, 15 February until Sunday, 1 March, Boris Johnson was on holiday at Chevening in Kent with his partner, Carrie Symonds. Reports emerged that he had asked for briefing notes to be kept short.

If it were not highly inappropriate in these pandemic times to spit, that is exactly what I would do as each day in this murderous chronology emerges from my magic bole.

On Tuesday, 18 February, Public Health England (PHE), the arm of the Department of Health with responsibility for testing and tracing contacts, reported to SAGE that they only had the capacity to cope with five COVID-19 cases a week. No more than fifty cases could be dealt with in any future scenario. The routine testing and tracing of contacts was therefore stopped.

These were political judgements, decisions that were dependent on a cost-benefit analysis. Senior government advisors had been present at every SAGE meeting.

This action to stop "test and trace" was the key reason why the UK had, by the end of May, the highest death rate in Europe.

On Thursday, 27 February, Professor Graham Medley informed SAGE members, in the presence of advisors from 10 Downing Street, that computer modellers had calculated a terrifying scenario in the UK of an eighty per cent infection of the population with five hundred thousand deaths. By now, the death toll in Italy, the first European country to be hit by the virus, was rising exponentially. The first lockdowns there had begun around 21$^{st}$ February.

The realisation was growing that the UK was just a few weeks behind Italy in the spread of the virus. But there was still time to learn from the experiences of the Italian pandemic.

On Friday, 28 February, officials confirmed the first case of virus transmission in the UK.

Boris Johnson returned from his holiday on Sunday, 1 March. He seemed unaware of the seriousness of the virus, saying, as he visited a hospital, that he understood coronavirus was a mild infection and the "vast majority will survive it very well". The behavioural advice from the PM is only centred on handwashing.

I really do have a strong urge to spit. My lungs are still fine, but my legs are so weary.

On Tuesday, 3 March, Boris Johnson made a television appearance in which he said that he had been at a hospital the day before and shaken hands with everyone, including coronavirus patients.

Some members of SAGE, we know, were horrified. "Absolutely bonkers!", was one response. Another scientist was "emotionally distraught", according to a colleague.

Their warnings were being ignored. The computer modellers were forecasting two hundred thousand dead even if measures to isolate the elderly, shut the schools and work from home were introduced.

These criminals in government knew what was on its way in much the same way as all of us might expect the tide to rise. The UK surge began the next day, Wednesday, 4 March. Officials announced the biggest one-day increase with thirty-four cases. The total of those infected soared to eighty-seven. The first UK fatality linked to COVID-19 occurred on Thursday, 5 March. This was no tide; this was a tsunami.

What they never got their heads around – and we are still struggling to do so – are all the consequences of a pandemic for every nook and cranny in our society and economy. They played with their bright ideas of achieving herd immunity and stealing a march on their competitors in the international markets, of striding manfully to the pedestal of world-beating success. Not for one second did it occur to them that they were opening a Pandora's box.

The evil clown leading this country into its killing fields will know all about the ancient Greek myth of Pandora's box. He read Classics at Oxford. Pandora was the first woman on earth. With a touch of appalling misogyny, the Greeks imagined Pandora as being created by the Gods as a punishment inflicted on humanity. Each one of the Gods gave her a gift, exquisite but tainted with evil. The box was never to be opened. Of course, as had to happen, Pandora's curiosity got the better of her and the world came to suffer all the evils that had been locked away in the casket.

Now, in some accounts of the myth, Pandora did manage to shut the magic box but not before all bar one of the tainted gifts had escaped. And the one that was left was Hope. A sublime double whammy for humanity if the box remains forever shut. I prefer a version in which Hope is released. We need that to counter the consequences of the narcissistic urgings of Johnson and his sidekick Cummings. He was also, as Johnson, a reader of Ancient History at Oxford. Interesting to speculate on why they should so savour the delights of playing at being Gods and wreaking death and destruction all over the land.

On Thursday, 5 March, Boris Johnson appeared on the TV programme, *This Morning*, and when asked whether delaying the coronavirus was about "flattening the curve" of the pandemic, he said:

> "That's where a lot of debate has been and one of the theories is that perhaps you could take it on the chin, take it all in one go and allow the disease, as it were, to move through the population, without taking as many draconian measures… I think it would be better if we take all the measures that we can now to stop the peak of the disease."

What might all that mean? Clarity is not among the PM's more developed skills. But that is deliberate. The man can bluster, with gusto. He can lie. And by being vague, he can avoid being caught in the headlights.

On Wednesday, 11 March, WHO declared a global pandemic. Rishi Sunak, the Chancellor of the Exchequer, delivered his first budget speech in which he proudly referenced the UK's "world-leading response to the coronavirus epidemic".

The next day, Thursday, 12 March, testing was officially confined to hospital patients. But they were in hospital because their symptoms were linked to COVID-19. This was absurd. The Government Chief Scientific Advisor Sir Patrick Vallance told *Sky News*:

> "We think this virus is likely to be one that comes year-on-year, becomes like a seasonal virus. Communities will become immune to it and that's going to be an important part of controlling this longer term. About sixty per cent is the sort of figure you need to get herd immunity."

But there is no scientific consensus on what percentage of the population would need to be infected to achieve herd immunity. Estimates vary from sixty per cent to ninety-five per cent. And there is no scientific certainty about how long any acquired immunity would last, anyway.

Beware a knight of the realm peddling mumbo jumbo as the Chief Scientific Advisor.

The scientists who understood the reality of the threat realised that the virus had been let go. The UK was sleepwalking into disaster. The unthinkable was happening.

There was now only one way to stop the virus from killing a million and more of the population: a national lockdown. All of us in quarantine. But within government, there was still the belief that the virus would be different here. English exceptionalism – that was the order of the day. We were, after all, world-beaters. The same dynamic that had powered Brexit would help see off this Chinese virus.

This is a magic episode in the mind games I play when running free. I am telling you the true chronological story years before the public inquiry report is published, whitewashing the unthinkable thing that has happened. The pursuit of herd immunity.

On Friday, 13 March, UK coronavirus cases rose by more than two hundred in a single day. Sporting authorities postponed events and fixtures. Yet the government did not move towards self-isolation and distancing. The population was still being advised only to wash their hands. An official denied that herd immunity was government policy, but the Italian prime minister Giuseppe Conte had a long phone conversation with Boris Johnson that Friday evening and concluded that Johnson wanted herd immunity. Sir Patrick Vallance, in a radio interview that same day, used the term "herd immunity" in explaining the government strategy.

On Sunday, 15 March, the day after the confirmed number of cases passed a thousand, Matt Hancock said the elderly could be quarantined for up to four months.

On Monday, 16 March, the UK's death toll rose to fifty-five, with 1,543 confirmed cases. WHO criticised countries who had not introduced testing:

"We have a simple message for all: test, test, test".

Johnson began to alter his message. "more social distancing is necessary"; "no unnecessary travel"; "start working from home where possible". He and Cummings were turning off the tap. The path to herd immunity needed adjustment. Testing and tracing programmes were now ramped up, days after the announcement that they were being largely abandoned.

The TomTom gizmo on my wrist faithfully records every one of the six thousand or so strides I make on my local circuit run. I have given you my truthful account of our descent into hell.

To revisit these last two months in this way is surreal. I find it scary to be this close to the paths that were followed and those that were not. I am not a digital games player but all that has happened feels rather like a mega-contrivance of computing genius that has gone hideously wrong. Those holding the controls were now way out of their depth. A significant group of scientists on the SAGE committee have been presenting an apocalyptic scenario since early February, and they have been ignored. The UK is now caught in limbo between the old normality and a full lockdown. The pubs and stores are still open; people are still commuting on the tube trains.

I find a touch of context helps the mind understand all the better. But sometimes, the body goes its own way. My body did that on Monday, 16 March. It was the day for the fortnightly recycling. Refuse collectors have remained key workers in this pandemic, always on duty. They would be arriving soon. My job was to get the bags and box out of the house and down the

steps to the edge of the front garden, ready for collection. I was rushing. My writing was urging my return. I remember pausing at the top of the steps, a red bag in my hand, leaning forwards, turning at the same time.

Now, I am falling. My balance has gone. I grasp the

Falling backwards down these steps, I glimpsed the world turning upside down inevitability of the loss of control. Even as I fall backwards and glimpse the world turning upside down, I sense this will be a hard landing. It is not the first time in the last year or two that the legs have gone from under me. My wrist had nearly cracked a year ago as I broke my fall with my hand.

I land on the back of my head. This could be serious. I monitored my position. I was still conscious. I lay very still and realised my hand had moved to the point of impact. It felt wet. The blood on my hand was not a good sign. Soon, people were gathering. I remember advising one of the first to arrive: 'Don't touch me! Don't get close.' COVID-19 was certainly on my radar.

Inside the ambulance, under examination, the questions kept coming. There was alarm when the paramedics asked me to confirm my age. 'Seventy-one,' I declared truthfully. 'Hang on, no, that's not right – I'm sixty-nine and three months.' They began to panic. My condition must have worsened. I sensed their alarm. 'Sorry,' I said. 'Only joking. It's just that with Hancock quarantining all those over seventy, I thought I'd better take a year or so off.' There was tangible relief. Their cargo was still in charge of his marbles.

I was back home by lunchtime. The large egg on my head had shrunk enough to justify an early exit, with neither brain scan nor stitches, from a hospital that was clearing the decks in preparation for the COVID-19 surge. It had been a weird experience being returned in an ambulance to the emergency department of the institution where I had been an outpatient for so long last year.

Now, though, I had once more returned safely home. I could continue to tease out what the hell was going on in my country. My running career was not yet over.

So, here I am, traversing the edge of this wide entrance to the farmhouse on the brow of the hill. It is only a few yards to the back of the sign for St Ives. The retracing of the steps in this COVID pandemic has taken us almost to the present. Just one more week to go. My duty is clear. Keep whistle-blowing.

On Tuesday, 17 March, Sir Patrick Vallance warned that as many as fifty-five thousand people may now be infected and said it would be a "good outcome" if the eventual death toll was below twenty thousand. During this week, as the NHS prepares to increase capacity to cope with the influx of patients with COVID-19, plans are further developed for the movement of fifteen thousand elderly patients back into care homes, but there is no provision for testing these patients before moving them.

We will learn that between a third and a half of all COVID-19 deaths have been in care homes. This game had slipped so grievously out of control.

A large number of labs across the country are offering the government help in testing, but their offers are met with messages of "we'll get back to you" and "it's not us you want; try this department". "It was like talking to a blancmange" one eminent scientist reported.

On Thursday, 19 March, the death toll rose to 144. Confirmed infections hit 3,269. There are, of course, thousands and thousands more cases.

On Friday, 20 March, it was announced that schools would be shut from Monday, but nothing else is scheduled for closure. Boris Johnson shared a phone conversation with President Emmanuel Macron, who had initiated a lockdown in France the previous Monday. Macron was adamant:

"This evening, at midnight, we will close the border with the UK unless you announce further measures to fight the pandemic."

That evening, at 8.00pm, Boris Johnson ordered all pubs, restaurants, gyms and other social venues across the country to close for the foreseeable future. But people were still allowed to go out and enjoy the sunshine that weekend.

So much for English exceptionalism! When Macron said "Jump!", Johnson jumped.

20th March was a Friday, and that day I had my weekly session with Ben, my physiotherapist, at the local sports centre. Ben has done wonders for my body over the last six years of my running. He knows all its secrets. This Friday's session was to be our last for a long time.

On Saturday, 21 March, there was news that the NHS had sealed a deal with private hospitals, securing almost twenty thousand staff and thousands of extra beds. That would have cost a packet, methinks. I am the socialist who has seen for the last three decades the creeping privatisation of the NHS. The UK death toll now stood at more than 230 people, with infection cases surpassing four thousand.

On Monday, 23 March, in a televised address, Boris Johnson proclaimed:

"From this evening I must give the British people a very simple instruction – you must stay at home."

The UK at long, long last had gone into lockdown. Well, almost. Dominic Cummings defiantly ignored the lockdown.

The door had been shut, but the virus had been given free rein for weeks already. The killer had bolted. The criminals at the centre of the UK government had decided to follow what the New Zealand Prime Minister Jacinda Ardern described as the "unthinkable" policy of achieving herd immunity. To steal an economic advantage over competitors in the world markets.

New Zealand is now virtually free from COVID-19. It acted fast and decisively. Here in the UK, the economy is sinking like a torpedoed ageing battleship, the victim of a misguided direct hit. The coffins of British citizens have mounted day by day, at first rapidly and then steadily.

My reverie snapped. I was struggling for breath now. So close to the summit, past the sign for St Ives, and still running. Unlike so many others who had struggled for breath in their fight against the virus.

On Monday, 23 March, the day lockdown was announced, I noted in my blog post that I had read Facebook posts criticising those who were "playing politics" and attacking "our leaders". I responded:

> *Please, please, please – if you think like that; if you think that this is a time we should all come together and our predicament takes us to a place beyond politics – read all my blog posts over the last few weeks... these are deeply political matters. Yes, we all need to come together but let's do so with political understanding.*

In that Monday blog post, I included information that I had discovered in the *Dorset Eye*, an online community magazine. A journalist, Tom Lane, had written an article infused with anger about the direction of government in general and the failings of Dominic Cummings in particular. Here is a taste:

> *To those of you who believe in this government, read this. This is why they left the schools open, this is why*

*pubs & restaurants only closed yesterday. You & your
family are the cattle in the herd.*

Tom Lane went on to highlight this passage from Tim
Shipman – the political editor of *The Sunday Times* and
a mainstream journalist who would have had access to
Downing Street – published in *The Sunday Times* the day
before, on Sunday, 22 March:

> Dominic Cummings, the prime minis-
> ter's senior aide, became convinced that
> Britain would be better able to resist a
> lethal second wave of the disease next
> winter if Whitty's prediction that 60% to
> 80% of the population became infected
> was right and the UK developed "herd
> immunity".
>
> At a private engagement at the end of
> February, Cummings outlined the gov-
> ernment's strategy. Those present say it
> was "herd immunity, protect the econ-
> omy and if that means some pensioners
> die, too bad".

This was a crack in the protective ring laid down by an
establishment who had seen Boris Johnson as the charismatic
politician who would save them from the threat of Jeremy
Corbyn and socialism. He had done so. But now, his list of
follies was lengthening.

This magic interlude in the ascent of my hill has been
joyless, apart from the intimation of dissent at the end. I have
been struggling for breath, and my limbs feel heavier and
heavier. And then I put myself and you through this tale of
madness. I will call it a day and just grit my teeth and make
it to the summit, to the peak of Little Trevalgan. I am still
running. I am still alive.

# 3

## SUMMIT THOUGHTS

The turning point at Little Trevalgan is just that. It is not a place to stop. Every time, the thrill of the turn and the sight of the sea fill me with joy. Why stop when you are running high on adrenalin? One more precious ascent to add to my list in this new age of pestilence. Seven times in April,

Looking towards Atlantic Bay from near the summit of Little Trevalgan

eight in May. We are now over halfway through June. Yet the question nags, deep down. How many more?

My guardian angels smother the speculation. You, as my companion, can address it more freely. The summer is now here; July is beckoning. Our misgoverned land is being nudged out of lockdown. The schools are opening, after a fashion. So too, businesses and shops. Wherever possible, keeping to a reading of the now more elastic rules of social distancing, England is returning to the old ways. The engine of the economy is being cranked.

England under Johnson is leading the way in the United Kingdom. "A world-beating performance", our leader has declared. Yet the leaders of the other nations in the UK – Wales, Scotland, and Northern Ireland – have enough autonomy not to follow too closely the madcap pace set by this English prime minister. Even as we neared the end of May, around eight thousand new cases of COVID-19 were being recorded each day in the UK. By the end of June, the figure for new cases was around three thousand, according to one academic estimate. No one can be quite sure. The margin of error is massive due to the obfuscation of the data.

Assuming only a two per cent fatality rate within a month of diagnosis, that means a steady, if decreasing, flow of bodies to the mortuaries of this country. Around 160 by the end of June, sixty by the end of July. All those corpses are the consequences of the cavalier welcome by Johnson and Cummings to a virus named COVID-19. Those bodies once had lives. Hopes, fears, dreams, families, all cut short. Then, funerals with the barest of rites, leaving families and friends with unfinished grieving and diminished meaning.

And those of us who have the measure of Johnson and his followers know with dreadful certainty what comes next. There will be a surge in new infections. A second peak is inevitable. And perhaps other peaks after that. There will be no full release of the statistical data that could identify these new outbreaks early enough to help mitigate their consequences. Deception and obfuscation will continue to be the order of the day. One fact only *The SKWAWKBOX* has revealed to date: the UK government has plans for tens of thousands more mortuary spaces. They are preparing for the second surge. Plans, no doubt, peppered with sub-contracts and profit-taking at every handover. Plans that might, perish the thought, need another public inquiry when this is all over, to stanch the smell of corruption.

My anger is surging right now as I turn for home, the Atlantic Bay ahead giving way to the more familiar bay of St Ives. In early June, the Johns Hopkins University in the USA issued a graph to show deaths per million from COVID-19

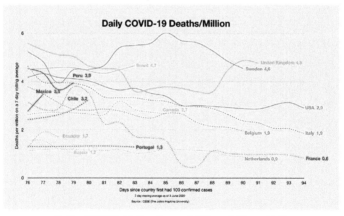

Daily COVID-19 Deaths per Million, 3rd June 2020
(The John Hopkins University, USA)

across the globe. The UK had the highest figure of any country in the world, even on the government's official figure of around forty thousand that more and more of us know is far lower than the real death toll of approaching sixty-five thousand – the number of excess deaths in our country. Only the USA, with a population five times the size of the UK's, has a larger total death toll.

You have been my companion for long enough now to know what happened, to understand the reasons. These deaths could have been avoided if Johnson had acted earlier. The lockdown could and should have been in place much earlier. There could and there should have been stocks of personal protective equipment in place. There could and there should have been an effective test, trace, and isolate system up and running, as advised by the World Health Organisation.

And yet, Johnson is pressing ahead with lockdown-easing measures that even the scientists who have chosen to collude know will push the death rate higher. All this, and the man who leads our diminished country still proclaims his great pride in all that he and his government have achieved.

As I turn, my thoughts are spilling over inside me.

There must be a reckoning. Those of us on the receiving end of injustice need to believe in the possibility of legal redress. Such rights have been long fought for. They are part of the fabric of a civilised society. They are the guarantors that our social and political institutions can continue to function and even flourish.

In my reading a couple of months ago, I learned of a Spanish senator who was attempting to take their prime minister to court on a charge of administrative malfeasance because of his government's failure to respond to the pandemic with the kind of rational and humane insight that other countries such as New Zealand have shown. Amen to that.

The resistance has begun to grow, in numbers and volume. But the need to expose the nakedness of the emperor becomes ever more pressing. In the first part of April, Dominic Cummings with wife and child had made a 260-mile journey from London to Durham, apparently while infected with coronavirus. And then, after recovery, the Cummings family travelled thirty miles from Durham to Barnard Castle to test father's ability to drive. All this, whilst the rest of us were in lockdown. At least six Church of England bishops were unequivocal in their social media condemnation of Mr Cummings. And the Bishop of Liverpool appeared in person on the BBC to agree with his colleagues. Goodness, how times change! The C of E used to be the Tory Party at prayer.

But for Johnson and Cummings, the Castor and Pollux presiding over our pandemic fate, such episodes are trivia, insubstantial matter to be brushed aside. What really counts is the easing of the lockdown so the wheels of the economy can turn again. Get the schools open so parents can be back at work. By the end of May, Johnson was claiming that there had been both a "consistent" reduction in deaths and a decline in new hospital admissions. Even as he spoke, there was a spike in the figures of deaths. Almost eight hundred bodies to the mortuary in just two days. And hospital admissions were nearly double that of the rate when Johnson announced the lockdown back in March.

Halfway through June, the government was forced into a U-turn over the issue of the schools reopening. Someone had calculated that there were eighty thousand people, regarded as "vulnerable", living in homes where there were children of primary school age. Too much roadkill. Yet now, I hear that all schools will reopen in September and parents who refuse to send their children back face being fined.

I know that people do not like being lectured. I do not want to harangue you. But please, let this turning point at Little Trevalgan be one timeless moment when you, my companion, come to understand this horror show more deeply. And, who knows? You may yet see the chickens coming home to roost. The neoliberal elites who have led the resurgence against all shades of socialism since the late 1970s may be preparing to ditch their Boris buffoon. Too much of a liability, this miscalculating clown responsible for the deaths of tens of thousands.

On Sunday, 7 June, Professor John Edmunds, a scientist who had been part of the SAGE advisory group back in early March, acknowledged in a television interview that "we should have gone into lockdown earlier… and it's cost a lot of lives".

Matt Hancock dismissed the claim. Well, he would, wouldn't he?

I spit.

My anger carries the fury of all those who must suffer these assaults on truth from hollow-skulled creatures who have crawled from their lairs to inhabit this political landscape. Theirs now by right, by dint of election success. Won by deception. And the cruelty of fate. My anger is blowing like a gale at the top of this hill as I feel in my body the depths of depravity and meanness that shape the lives of so many across the world.

Looking up towards the summit of Little Trevalgan

I need to take care not to lose you, my companion, in this outpouring of mine. Extremists, once outed, are ripe for shunning. Calling out the misdeeds in society has always been a tricky business. Take those Old Testament prophets, for instance. Eight hundred years before the time of Jesus, Hosea told the truth to his people, straight from the heart, in the name of Yahweh:

> *Listen to this... you who are responsible for justice.*
> *They are entrenched in their deceitfulness and so I am*
> *going to punish them all.*

Hosea was the prophet of doom. But always in his messaging there was the promise that things could get so much better.

Always there is hope.

My anger is a white anger.

In the big picture, black anger has deeper roots and even more justification.

African anger; Afro-Caribbean anger.

Angers that come from being screwed twice. Once as a victim of white imperialism, white colonialism, and white racial scapegoating. And then again, as part of the multi-ethnic masses. Those who are black and white and all colours. Those who comprise the labour force in the caring, retail, transport, hospitality and what is left of the manufacturing sectors. Those who are underpaid and live out their existence in overcrowded, overpriced rented accommodation. In sum, those who are turned over and used by the white and wealthy elites who control the levers of power, the infamous 0.1%, to use the calculation of Noam Chomsky, the great American linguist and activist.

Why should such thoughts be filling my head? I am not black. True. But I did spend over half a decade working to right injustice in an institutionally racist setting in London in the 1970s and 1980s. Black Lives Matter.

Something awful, something truly terrifying, happened on 25th May last month which brought all these angers to boiling point. A white American policeman killed a black man, George Floyd, in Minneapolis in the USA by kneeling on him for eight minutes and forty-two seconds. A bystander filmed this execution – a lynching, 21st century-style – and then the world watched, too.

"I can't breathe."

"I can't breathe."

"I can't breathe."

These repeated words of the dying forty-six-year-old father became an anthem of anger across the globe.

Here in England, the statue erected to honour a slave trader who had helped make Bristol rich was torn down one weekend in June. This, at the same time as a government report was being belatedly published, showing the far higher coronavirus fatality rates among Black, Asian and minority ethnic (BAME) communities. Presented with all its recommendations removed. The case studies that underpinned its findings also missing.

This incidence of institutional racism within the highest echelons of government has happened under the smokescreen provided by the COVID-19 pandemic. There is ample evidence for Johnson's studied racial disparagement of black people. His racism goes deep with his talk of "watermelon smiles" and "picaninnies".

How can a man as sad as this and as mad as this and as bad as this be where he now is?

The unthinkable becomes possible because the 0.1% know how to milk a crisis. Johnson has been lifted high on the back of a slogan:

"Get Brexit done!"

The likes of Johnson and Cummings must feel impregnable. On top of the world. At the summit of their endeavours. Like me. May their pride go before their fall. I will keep digging into my reserves of knowledge and reading to expose them.

Those now in power have the means to censor reports of social inequality and structural racism. They can bury stuff with seeming impunity. The truly shocking becomes a one-day news item that will soon be forgotten in the noise of battle against the virus. Every crisis is an opportunity for the neoliberal capitalists to cement their power.

Naomi Klein, the Canadian activist, nailed it in 2007 with her idea that free-market politicians will deliberately use a strategy of "shock therapy" to initiate changes that would previously, in normal circumstances, have been unthinkable. Crises create the distractions, emotional and physical, that can provide the smokescreen for dramatic change. COVID-19 certainly fits that bill.

Even before Klein, the American radical academic Herbert Marcuse had sussed it. He had seen how smart the elites can be in using the levers of control their power has given them. In 1964, in his book, *One Dimensional Man*, Marcuse concluded that:

> *Nothing indicates that it will be a good end. The economic and technical capabilities of the established societies are sufficiently vast to allow for adjustments and concessions to the under-dog, and their armed forces sufficiently trained and equipped to take care of emergency situations.*

Yet all is not gloom.

Marcuse allowed the last words to rest with the German Jewish philosopher, Walter Benjamin:

> *It is only for the sake of those without hope that hope is given to us.*

Hope, I reflect at this turning point, is my essence. May it be for all those who value humanity. Walt Whitman, the American poet, was there when he wrote of the flag of his disposition that had been woven out of the "hopeful green stuff". My hopeful green stuff is still visible even in this darkness.

I hope that neither Louise nor I fall victim to this deadly virus.

I hope that we are not added to the death list created by this moronic buffoon who presides over this country.

I hope the death rate will fall to zero.

I hope we can become New Zealand.

But that last hope is never going to happen.

I can, though, hope that more and more of our citizens will come to understand what has been done by Boris Johnson, the man who most preferred to Jeremy Corbyn – the alternative leader on offer – at the last General Election in December 2019.

And I can hope that our citizens will come to have some inkling of what an opportunity they lost and how similar our island story would have been to New Zealand's if Jeremy had become the prime minister.

Maybe, just maybe, my hope that Johnson will get his comeuppance and we will have justice is coming good. The blanket aversion of the mainstream media to telling the truth about what has happened seems to be breaking down. Criticism is audible in the airwaves and in cyberspace. Scientists are breaking cover and denying the version of "truth" presented by those amongst their community who have shared public platforms and weasel words with our political leaders, echoing their falsehoods.

The editor of *Mirror Politics* has commented that, in the past, even a handful of excess deaths in hospitals would have prompted calls for resignations, but now we have a situation where the prime minister has failed abysmally in his duty of care and there is barely a shrug of the shoulders. Well put. But where were the critical voices before now?

Listen to Yasmin Alibhai-Brown, writing in the mainstream *i* newspaper on 9th June:

*Does one pity them, or maul them? Chris Whitty, Sir Patrick Vallance, Jenny Harries and other medical and scientific experts show up at coronavirus press briefings to be used as patsies by the elected junta running Britain… every policy – from flip-flopping on masks, to lockdown, to opening up, to test and trace – has been shambolic and a danger to the public.*

Thank goodness there was editorial clearance for that extraordinary act of truth-telling. Better late than never. And then, on 11th June, another member of the SAGE group, Professor Neil Ferguson, acknowledged that had lockdown happened a week earlier, the death toll would have been reduced by at least a half.

And the response of the UK prime minister to having the scientific ground cut from under his feet?

"Of course, we are going to have to look back on all this and learn lessons. But a lot of these questions are still premature. There are lots of things, lots of data, things that we still don't know."

Johnson and Cummings will do whatever they can to avoid the legal consequences of their decisions. I see them back at their cauldron, still cross-dressed as witches, spitting out magic spells and incantations to prevent us from discovering that they were the wicked warlocks behind the potion labelled "herd immunity" and that it will be the order of the day until the vaccine arrives.

This turning point has gifted me this opportunity to reach into the magic trunk and grasp from the bole these tales of rage and hope. Over the last weeks, from the close of May through to now, the end of June, the regal foxgloves have appeared in the hedgerow. They stand purple and tall, symbols of beauty and grace. Now, as July beckons, they are drooping a little. Within a week or two, they will be a memory. That is the way of the world. It is our way.

But it was not the way followed by tens of thousands of British citizens who have now become a memory. There was nothing natural about their passing.

# 4

## A GOOD RESULT

'I wish I could still run.'

The words had come from the cyclist moving steadily past me on my left as I ran uphill, keeping to the right, all the better to see the whites of the eyes of the drivers coming towards me. You can feel very vulnerable as a flesh-and-blood runner. It was a relief to experience so little traffic for so long during lockdown. But now, the business of a Cornish summer is returning.

I had glimpsed, from behind, the muscular and wiry legs of this athletic male crouched over his handlebars, intent, like me, on reaching the top. It must have been his knees that had failed him. Or perhaps he was just being kind to the white-haired old man labouring uphill.

And yet, here I am indeed running. Downhill. Oh my! This is good! We are now halfway through July. We have moved into the second half of 2020. And I am alive.

A year ago, in 2019, I was running this circuit every Sunday morning for seven consecutive Sundays from 28th

July to 8th September. It was my only run each week. A celebratory run.

Wait!

What are those, over there to the left, almost on the horizon, in that furthest field? They are back! That narrow strip of acreage is filled with motionless forms, brushed in shades of whiteness by the morning sunlight. The carapaces of urban dwellers are with us once more. A cluster of their mobile homes and caravans. Those touches of red and blue are the cars that brought them to this distant field. I imagine a shimmer of mist above their communal nest, alive with dreams of odyssey and release. These are our "emmets", the sunburned red ants of modern Cornish legend. The tourists have returned, the backbone of the local economy. They have answered the call of duty from No.10.

But who took their temperatures when they arrived on campsite? Who administered their COVID-19 tests as they pulled up to their resting place for the next week or two? Not the farmer who owns the field, smart enough to have added a touch of diversification to his agribusiness. Not the local authority, pummelled into poverty and ineffectiveness after a decade of austerity. Not the central government, for sure.

The Grim Reaper is smiling with anticipation. There must be at least another half-dozen similar sites around St Ives. Most people have had enough of isolation by now. They are being nudged to follow their desire for release. Johnson is talking up the possibility of this pestilence being over by Christmas.

Does he have no sense of irony? The boys were saying the same thing in 1914 when their European war had only just begun. Or are Johnson and Cummings using the irony of sociopaths, revelling in the fruits of their murderous cauldron concoctions? Their mad pursuit of herd immunity will be the unspoken order of the day until sometime next year when the vaccine finally arrives, and protection does become possible.

Up here, still this close to the summit, I am in the sky. I am air-bound, in the realm of souls and spirits. Below me, there is the land and the sea. Earth and water. Here there is a coming together. This is elemental.

It is all a question of perspective. Sometimes on a run, when the cloud cover forms, this unity is broken. I cannot see above me. The sea has disappeared. I can only imagine such harmony through the filter of my memory. And often, even when daylight is delivering wonderful and breath-catching clarity, the background interference of a cluttered mind means the vision never takes full form. A glimpse only of that elusive awakened state of consciousness when life reveals its full meaning.

The English playwright Denis Potter made a film of his dying days in 1994 as he succumbed to liver cancer. There is a moment when he bursts into ecstasy as he sees from the window of his home the spring blossom of the cherry tree in the garden.

'Oh my!' he exclaims. 'The whitest white of white! There has never been such whiteness!'

The dying time does help sharpen the vision.

I wish we could all learn to see with such brilliance.

I shut my eyes as the fifteen stone weight of my own body propels me forwards, downhill, my stride pattern quickening. Time to return to those celebratory Sunday runs last year. Where shall I begin? This is difficult. I have been in the closet for such a long time.

Let me begin at the church. That church, down there. Its tower is a local landmark. Nearly two hundred years ago, there were Christian believers in the village of Halestown, unseen below me, who favoured the Anglican way of following the teachings of Jesus. They wanted to build a church in their village. But all the local land-owning farmers were Christians who preferred the Methodist way of understanding the Good News. They refused to sell any of their land for the building of an Anglican church. A generation or so later, the Anglicans of Halestown did get to build their church – St John's in the Fields – down there, my church, a couple of miles away. They had found a farmer prepared to sell a field or two. A Sunday walk to church was an added blessing.

Looking towards the church and the B3306
from near the summit of Little Trevalgan

Louise, decided to attend the Sunday services at this church of St John's, the nearest to our home, before I did. Neither of us had set foot within a church for nearly seven years. We were not feeling diminished. Something I said in the middle of October 2018 had triggered this return of hers to a church community. And I was responding to what I had been told.

Louise arranged to see the vicar. He listened as she explained, late one afternoon in the vicarage, that she would be coming to church now and I might follow, keeping her company, after the London marathon in April 2019 had been run. I was following a long-run training schedule on Sundays and would not be joining her just yet.

'Rob has been diagnosed with cancer. Prostate cancer.'

The vicar listened with professional calm and empathy.

You see, these runs of mine, this magical run which you are sharing with me, all this is about dying. And acceptance. And not accepting. And fighting against a dying that is not in the natural order.

If I were to die of my cancer, that would be in the natural order. Cancer is part of nature. Our body is made up of cells that live and die. Cell death is natural and beneficial. Apoptosis. It is a normal and controlled part of an organism's growth and development. We are programmed by nature for cellular death and replacement. Cells need to die so the body can replace them with new cells that function better.

But some cells do not want to listen. They are the naughty ones. No way am I going to die just because I am supposed to!

A conspiracy of rebellion is hatched.

Abnormal cell growth begins.

Did you really think we were ready to die?!

Eat your heart out, loser!

We will continue to grow.

We will continue to divide.

And we will do this together.

Our unity is our strength.

I can almost feel sorry for these cells of mine that have gone rogue. They want to hang on to life. I wonder if they realise that their pathway carries its own regulator. They are fated to die no matter what. Their wild bid for freedom, if left unchecked, will end with the death of the body. The body in which they live and have their being. The temple shall come crashing down and all within will perish. That is the case. The natural order of things.

Or of course, they may find their pathways through the body blocked by the counterattacks of medical science. We have dared to take on nature. We have, after all, split the atom.

My naughty cancer cells met their Waterloo thanks to the advances in urology. I have been so lucky. A diagnosis of cancer is a fast-track ticket in our National Health Service. At the end of October 2018, less than two weeks after the blood test had revealed a PSA (prostate specific antigen) score of 203, I was tucked away and held tight in a whole-body scanner as the rays probed the extent of the incursions of the rogue cells. A day later, my medical team were celebrating the results.

'We didn't expect the rest of the body to be clear of cancer, to be honest. Not with the PSA score you had. You have had the cancer for at least a year. Possibly two years.'

My guardian angels exchanged glances.

The consultant on the telephone continued:

'A cancer is, as you know, an abnormal cell growth that has the potential to invade and spread to other parts of the body. Yours hasn't. Well, a little bit around the lymph glands surrounding your prostate.'

He paused.

'We'll deal with that through radiotherapy later, but now we'll start the drug treatment to wipe out your testosterone, your anabolic hormones which increase protein synthesis. That's the name we give to the process in which cells make proteins. We don't yet understand how, but we will one day. Your rogue cancer cells are hitching a lift on your testosterone. Eliminate them and we stop the spread. We call this hormone ablation. Your testosterone levels will take a nosedive. Testosterone is a hormone that controls the development and growth of the sexual organs, including the prostate gland.'

He paused, again.

'Any questions?'

I was not going to die within weeks. There would be time for treatment. My guardian angels were celebrating with high fives.

Yet only a few weeks ago, I had not even known where my prostate was, let alone what it did. Or what it looked like. We are ignorant of so much until necessity educates us.

Here, on this wondrous descent, with the bay of St Ives filling my vision, I am running free, swinging my arms up and back and round again, first the left arm, then the right arm. My mouth opens and the cry of joy hits the silence around me.

'Yes!'

'Yes!'

'Yes!'

My homage to Molly Bloom and the literary orgasm that sent a sparkle of delight dancing through my late teens testosterone-charged body as I read James Joyce's masterpiece: *Ulysses*.

The moorland to my right, with its straddle of giant granite tors towering on the skyline, soaks up my ecstasy in an instant. Likewise, the fields to my left. This landscape will be here long after I have passed on.

I am so lucky.

Lucky.

Lucky.

Lucky.

I can see the bend ahead, the road curling in and disappearing, then reappearing. Some danger here. A runner needs to have their wits about them. Listening, looking, calculating which side is the safest to be running on. Last week, I was running down and had reached the elbow of the bend when I heard the siren and saw, appearing over the top of the hedge-line, flashing blue lights. The eyes of a monster tonnage, unseen, racing towards me. A second later, the bright red fire engine roared into full view. I shrank into the hedge and raised my hand in submission. The fireman driver acknowledged my presence as his vehicle filled the road passing by.

We are so vulnerable as a species. No matter how clever we think we are.

I have still got quite a few more strides to make before that bend. More magic bole time.

It was Christmas 2018. The clinical nurse on the other end of the telephone line was speaking.

'Let's see. At the last count, your PSA score was 203. And now it is…'

A pause followed, so pregnant I could imagine the baby grinning with delight at its imminent release.

'One.'

We shared a chuckle. This was, as she later said, "a good result". Another release on death row.

I continued my training for the London marathon in April 2019. On the last day of 2018, I saw my consultant and was offered a combination of chemotherapy and radiotherapy. I turned down the chemo. Opting for the chemical path would have meant kissing goodbye to my marathon challenge.

My medical team then helped even more by holding back on scheduling the radiotherapy until after the London event. But it was touch and go whether I got to the starting line, let alone completed the race. The hormone treatment drug, Zoladex, was working a treat in reducing my PSA score. Unfortunately, it was playing havoc with my knees.

Ben, my physio, is so skilled. And I was so determined. In the end, I got my London 2019 finisher's medal. It took fifty minutes longer to complete than in 2017, and I became rather emotional at the finish, but I had another marathon to add to the list.

I did also become a member of the congregation at St John's church, joining Louise. But I remained in the closet. I did not want people seeing me through the filter of cancer. Members of Louise's birth family were told when I was first diagnosed. Louise would turn to them first if I died. But no one local knew except for Ben and the vicar and his curate, who bumped into me one morning at the hospital where I was having my thirty-seven sessions of radiotherapy, every day, five days a week, for seven and a half weeks through July and August 2018. Yes, the same hospital I returned to by ambulance after my fall down the steps.

You can see why my Sunday runs from July through to August in 2019 were celebratory.

# 5

## GLOBAL MATTERS

The gradient of the road changes as I get closer still to the bend ahead. Running upwards, this section slows me. Now, it excites me. I glance across to the hedgerow on my left where I saw for the first time, last week, a single tufted vetch plant, tall-stemmed and spiked with scores of bluish-purple flowers. There! I glimpse it again. Singular and so beautiful: a miniature foxglove, tailored for fairy folk.

Another quick look, taking care to adjust the balance. The head tilts to the left. This time, my glance is over the hedgerow. Yes. The grey granite stones, relics of a civilisation whose bones lie buried deep around me, are still there. And today, there are sheep, bright in their white-washed fleeces, grazing in the foreground of the field. In the distance, I can see the farmhouse and its barns, a thin edge on that ancient land.

Then, the solar panels fill my vision. So often we look and see and miss the obvious. I have never noticed these panels before. Are they new?

Humanity being clever again. Catching the energy of our primal life force, the sun. It is a much more satisfying cosmology to believe that we are in orbit around the sun, rather than the other way round. One day, of course, the sun will eat us up. For breakfast. But that is in a long, long distant time and part of the natural order of things.

What worries me,
When I care to think
About it,
Is the prospect
Of irreversible
And unnatural
Global extinction
Within a decade
If we do not pull
The emergency cord
Right now
And start turning the world
Of the wealthy and powerful
Upside down
And creating a green revolution
In the economy
And society.

Please do not tire of my passion for calling out injustice and sounding warning bells. I am the prophet, soaked in Hebrew wisdom. And please allow me to reclaim the word "passion". I cringe when I hear people talk about how passionate they are. "I have always been passionate about education", they say. Or "we are passionate about delivering your needs". They mean we care about getting your vote. We care about getting your business. Passion has been hijacked. I make my case for reclaiming true passion. Such passion means suffering. The Passion of Christ. The passion of a people facing global extinction. That is something to be passionate about.

A green and socialist revolution. Non-violent, of course. Now, that would be a natural and life-affirming response to this utterly unnatural way of dying that lies ahead. I am, you see, putting my trust and my hope in the survival instinct of the species. If you do not, you remain part of the problem.

So many good causes to follow and defend. And you never know what lies around the corner.

I have almost reached my bend. The road to Little Trevalgan branches off to my left. Today is hot. I am wet with sweat. My focus switches back to the fly that has been bugging me for the last few seconds. In these years of summer running, I have fashioned a theory about flies which embraces their territorial range and the games they play. My basic tenet is that flies like fun. A lot of life forms love a bit of good-natured humour. Our dog, Ella, does. She will lie still on the bed and then make a mock-snap at me as I pass by, before gently jumping off. This fly that has fastened on my face has won that honour from within the ranks of his fly community. He now has the best part of three minutes to make my life as interesting as possible before I pass through the perimeter doors of his fly republic and escape his joyous attention.

My fly is into orifices. It attempts an entry into my ear. The way is barred. Then my nostrils. It fails again. I can feel it thinking: *Am I bothered? This is fun!* It tries my eyes, behind my glasses. Too difficult. Ah! Up and under my chin and then the lips.

A golden rule for runners in summertime in countryside such as mine: keep your mouth shut.

It is such a persistent little bug, this fly of mine. The creature seems intent on prising my lips apart by tickling with its wings. It fails. It tries again. It fails. Time up! A final ceremonial hover and then I am through the door of its world. Until I return.

I should acknowledge that one of its kind did meet a rather terrible fate some three weeks previous, and I was unwittingly involved. I was running uphill at the time and nearing the top. The winds were out in force, offshore, and I was struggling against them. The sun was high. My thoughts were centred on coronavirus threats.

My mouth fell open, and from nowhere, this unfortunate fly was blown helter-skelter into the fatal orifice. I choked. Immediately transformed into an agency for COVID-19, this poor insect was retched up dead. I lived to tell the tale, but since then, my lips have been even more tightly sealed when running. Is my paranoia due to my age? Have I been nudged into seeing myself as especially vulnerable to this new virus that seems intent on reshaping the world?

I remember the best Oxford lecturer of them all, James Campbell, a don from Worcester College, explaining with some relish in 1968 that the Black Death had been brought to England carried by the fleas that lived on the backs of the black rats – "rattus rattus" – that had hitched their lifts on board the ships that docked in English ports. No surprise that insects have taken root in my subconscious as instruments of death. One in three subjects copped it in those bubonic times back in the 14th century. Now that was a real plague.

I do need these perspective skills I learned as an

embryonic historian. I am living here in Cornwall in the safest part of the country. London has had nearly three times as many cases of COVID-19, so too the south-east. The north-west has had three and a half times as many and heads the field. The early fear of my imminent demise through infection is fading. Yet an infection is an infection. A death is a death. And this roadkill is unnatural. It is man-made. Made by two men. Johnson and Cummings.

My running stride now is smooth. I could run for ever like this. Downhill. The weight of my own body propelling me forwards. Almost effortless. Another glance towards the hedgerow on my left. Over these last couple of months, these green thickets that separate field from road have grown taller and wider. The bends have become more dangerous. Drivers see my running form later. My body is more at risk. But what wonderful homes they make for such an array of wild flora. The blackberries have flowered by now and their fruit has started to form. Along this stretch, the colour orange is exploding. Crocosmia. Gardeners call this flowering iris: "Coppertips". A garden centre plant gone rogue. In this, our Penwith peninsula, summer is painted orange. I love the fact that crocosmia is a migrant from Africa.

Time for more tales from the bole depository.

A friend of mine, David, lives in London in the borough of Brent. I have devoted a blog post to his story. He has a measure of wisdom having lived with Duchenne's muscular dystrophy for all his sixty years. Neither his sister nor brother, who both had this genetic condition, made it past thirty years. He is entitled to feel vulnerable during a time of plague.

David sent me an article from *The Guardian* newspaper in

late June this year. It reported that at least thirty-six residents had died in Church End, a small estate of deprivation in north Brent with a large British-Somali population. That makes it the second worst cluster in the country. Brent can claim the highest coronavirus death rate in England and Wales. Excess deaths in the borough are three times the national average.

A third of employees in Brent earn below the London living wage. A third of households claim housing benefit. One in six are in fuel poverty. Social inequalities are deeply entrenched. Waves of immigrants have settled in Brent over the centuries, but ever since Thatcher acted to cut back council housing in the 1980s, these newcomers have ended up in houses and flats owned by private landlords. Some of this accommodation is not fit for habitation and much is too small for its occupants. Most of these people paying rent are BAME. We are back in George Floyd territory. We are in the shadow of the Grenfell Tower death by fire and smoke ordeal. Yes. Black Lives Matter.

Young people struggle to find the space and internet access to continue their education when they get home. Overcrowded living conditions blight lives. Many of those Church End workers who died were on the frontline: carers, bus drivers, cleaners, postal workers, shopkeepers and taxi drivers. Without PPE, some picked up the virus and brought it back home, unwittingly infecting parents and grandparents. In multi-occupancy homes, families may have no option other than to share toilets and kitchens.

And here am I running through an officially designated Area of Outstanding Natural Beauty. I pass the sign, set in granite, declaring this self-evident truth every time I begin my ascent of this hill. But it is the darkness of Brent that is filling my mind as I ease my way into this first stretch of the bend. Welcome to pandemic Brent. We are witnessing a reworking of William Blake's "dark, satanic mills". A counterpoint to "England's green and pleasant land".

Forty plus years ago, in 1977, I began my seven years of service as the head of the history department at Aylestone school in Brent. Within a week, the sweat had burnt my skin. Back then, there were over 1,400 students on roll. Eighty-five per cent Afro-Caribbean, ten per cent Asian, five per cent Caucasian. By the time I left the school, numbers had shrunk to less than seven hundred, these falling rolls largely the result of Thatcher's immigration policies. Fewer pupils but still a challenge. The main difficulty remained as it had been at the start: the low expectations of most of the largely Caucasian teaching staff. It was, of course, unrecognised "institutional racism". But the term itself had little currency until 1999 when Sir William Macpherson, in his report into the racist killing of Stephen Lawrence in Eltham, London, labelled the Metropolitan Police as "institutionally racist".

I grew up in a racist family. Most of my generation did. My family's suburban fears and memories of empire ensured that white lives would always matter more. My decision to take the job at Aylestone was no doubt in part another two-fingered gesture towards my father, who by now had extracted himself from any connection with his fractious son. But it was also a chance to put into further practice my discovery that teachers' expectations do indeed help determine pupil performance. And year after year, the exam results of the students taught by me and my team of two showed the force of that self-evident truth. In 1977, the history exam results at Advanced Level recorded one grade D pass and five fails. And at Ordinary

Level, twelve passes at grades C to A and sixteen passes at grades D to E. A year later, our first set of results were in. Five passes at Advanced Level with two grade Bs, one grade C, one grade E, and no fails. And at Ordinary Level, twenty-nine passes at grades C to A and seventeen passes at grades D to E. The geography exam results were two passes at Ordinary Level in 1977 and three Ordinary Level passes in 1978.

But there were others too, bringing meaning to lives of colour. In 1978, a BAME teacher was the driving force behind a breathtaking production of *West Side Story* that made our hearts sing. Louise had travelled with me from Windsor in Berkshire, where we lived, to see the show.

I got to know David, my friend in Brent, when he was a student in my A-level history class in the early 1980s. My school had become Aylestone community school as pupil numbers fell. In 1984, I left, and soon after, the school got

1X1, my 1st year form, at Aylestone School in 1978,
with a couple of intruders on the right-hand end of the back row.

another makeover and became Queen's Park community school. Three and a half decades later, on Sunday, 8 March this year, Rhoda Ibrahim, a Queen's Park community leader in her late fifties, was celebrating International Women's Day. Her group had arranged a talk by a barrister, who had been raised on benefits in the local community, about the many barriers to social mobility in London. The location was Queen's Park community school, my alma mater.

The nation should have already been in lockdown. But it was not. Later that day, her friend Hassan Farah drove her home from the school I know so well. It lies a stone's throw from David's house. Hassan was a local teacher, widely credited for helping four British-Somali students from Brent gain Oxbridge places. A day or so later, Rhoda Ibrahim, Hassan Farah and several other attendees that afternoon fell ill with coronavirus symptoms. Rhoda survived. Hassan died six weeks later.

The severity of the virus did not dawn on the community until too late. Abdillahi Mohamed, who runs an office in Church Road, reported that information was not made available in Somali early enough. In effect, people were abandoned. Rhoda Ibrahim soon found the support system was in total collapse. Once recovered, she was doing the same work as she had done on the frontline with UNCR in refugee camps in Ethiopia, Djibouti and Yemen in the early '90s. Victoria Ling, who was born and raised in the borough and works there as a nurse in a GP practice, still struggles to comprehend the scale of suffering:

"I was talking to patients who would say my aunt has died, my uncle has died, my dad has died. It was literally every day."

Remember the basics. Johnson and Cummings are responsible for allowing this pandemic entry into the United Kingdom. COVID-19 is a natural virus. But this death toll is unnatural. We should rage against the dying of the light when the extinguishing hand behaves with deliberate intent. And grieve for those in Brent and elsewhere who fell victim to a murderous economic ideology shaped by stupidity and arrogance.

But always there is hope. There is the hope that is linked to the vaccines that are being developed to protect against COVID-19. And there is the hope that fuels the actions of those who give their time and money and creative energies to the struggle to save the ecosystem that keeps us alive. They have read the runes and know that we have a decade left before the threat of global extinction becomes a reality.

My voice is in their service. My runner's thoughts may convey truths that are hard to swallow, but they remain ripe for sharing. In our circumstances, we need soothsayers.

Extinction Rebellion was established as a global environmental movement in May 2018 with the aim of using non-violent civil disobedience to compel governments to avoid crossing the tipping points in the earth's ecosystem and so plummeting us towards ecological catastrophe. In November of that year, members of the movement blockaded five bridges across the Thames to help get their message across to the nation. By then, my focus of attention had turned to matters of personal survival. My prostate cancer had just been diagnosed. But Extinction Rebellion and I still had a date to share in our diaries.

Fast forward nine months and I am arriving each day at the RCH, the Royal Cornwall Hospital, for my dose of radiotherapy. Imagine my reactions as I overheard – one day in early August after my treatment – these words exchanged in a hospital corridor as I made my way out.

'They have come to protest against his visit.'

'Who are they?'

'It's Extinction Rebellion. That new group.'

'How did they get to hear about the PM's visit?'

'Heaven alone knows! They must have some very well-placed people. We didn't know until six this morning.'

And there they were! I almost ran as I moved forwards to join them. Very soon, at around 10.30am, I became part of the line-up. Within minutes, I had been delegated to fetch a placard for my personal use from a stockpile some distance away. But I misunderstood the precise location and found myself attempting to talk to a small group of people clustered together in the shade of a clump of trees about thirty yards

Global Extinction demonstration outside the Royal Cornwall Hospital, Truro – image taken by photojournalist, James Pearce

away. Observers from the hospital staff taking advantage of a coffee break to get a look at the action, or so I thought. A female vicar. A medic with a stethoscope. A couple of porters. And a guy with a walkie-talkie. They said little and they did not seem too keen on my sudden arrival. No, they did not know where the placards were. The guy with the walkie-talkie turned his back and started a conversation in a low voice. I felt uncomfortable and retreated to my comrades who told me where I should have gone.

Dead on the dot of 12.00pm, the convoy we had been waiting for appeared. No one attempted to rush out in front of the cars. That had been decided beforehand. And the police informed. No doubt, whichever wing of the security forces I had stumbled on by glorious mischance also knew too. The female vicar was a nice touch, though, but she was so unfriendly. She needs to have more role play training. And

The UK prime minister makes his exit from the Royal Cornwall Hospital, Truro, passing the Global Extinction demonstrators – image taken by photojournalist, James Pearce

that is as close as I have ever got to the man who has got away with murder. So far.

I meet other dog walkers when I am out with Ella, and they tell me stories that they have been told of what life is like these days in the centre of St Ives. The centre I no longer dare enter. I hear there is little social distancing. Few facemasks worn, except now in shops and even there, not always. A mass of swirling humanity in narrow lanes. Being on holiday has always brought out for many a letting go, a disregard for the straitjacket of normal conventions. That I understand. But now the stakes are so high.

I go online and watch the video evidence as it attracts Likes and Anger responses on a local website. "The Day of the Emmets" has come to town, showing now in glorious Panavision. The locals who are serving behind their shop counters are right to be scared. Masks can slip. The local economy may be mending, but those who launched this herd immunity caper know what they are doing. This virus is being fed, not eliminated.

# 6

## VIRAL FLOWS

Oh my! What a month this has been. On Monday, 7 September, the mainstream media were covering the news that nearly three thousand new cases of COVID-19 had been reported in the UK, the largest daily figure since 22nd May. Another headline that day announced that a world-record ninety thousand new cases had been recorded in India the day before, on Sunday, 6 September. Assuming a two per cent mortality rate, that means in a month's time, there will be some sixty coronavirus deaths in the UK and 1,800 in India. Since this is clearly the start of a second surge of infection, expect a rapid movement of the figures upwards. A week earlier, on 31st August, I saw a headline reporting that COVID-19 cases around the world had passed twenty-five million.

Movement is my saving grace. Being a runner is vital to my remaining fully alive. The nurse in the Cornwall prostate team expressed it well in an online message:

*I am so impressed that you are running, even if it is a*

*bit slower – it is absolutely the best thing for you to be doing – all the harder while on the hormone treatment so even more of an achievement. I hope you are keeping safe – such strange times.*

By Thursday, 10 September, the strangeness of our times was only too clear in newspaper headlines. The Johnson and Cummings roadshow was playing once more with the taps of their herd immunity project. And their Brexit adventure was being ratcheted up a gear. The cauldron of chaos was bubbling nicely.

The laws governing our social movement had now been adjusted to limit the flow of the virus. No more than six people could meet at any one time, indoors or outdoors, for the next six months, except for weddings and funerals. The Rule of Six. Government plans were well established to cope with an increase in funerals in the coming months. Remarkable foresight. So why was such talent – and money – not being used to stop this pandemic in its tracks?

International law was now being broken in an unprecedented manner to ease our movement away from Europe and into glorious Brexit isolation. Our country had become a rogue state. Perfidious Albion, for all to see. A misgoverned state with seventy thousand excess deaths, more than anywhere else in the world, per head of population.

I am on the last leg of this double bend in the road. Here, the gradient seems to rise slightly, even though I am descending. In fifty or so paces, I will be passing the left turn to Trowan and then the long, long downwards stretch to the next gentle bend and the beginning of the pavement. Forget the bigger picture. Time for a reverie.

It must be nearly a year since my medication was switched from Zoladex to Decapeptyl. Another hormone treatment drug. Every three months, I walk down to the Stennack surgery for my jab.

Same outcome each time, thank goodness. My testosterone levels remain untraceable. My lower limbs are still stiff and demanding exercise.

The cause of all this has not gone away, though. My prostate cancer has a medical label to identify its degree of severity. On the Gleason scale, it registers as a five out of six. The most severe is six out of six. But on the bright side, the cancer has been constrained.

Oh, so lucky!

Lucky.

Lucky.

Lucky.

These three-monthly jabs do give my lower limbs jip. But a little creaking and wincing as I lower myself to my knees in preparation for my warm-up exercises is a small price to pay.

And if I had not been a runner with the desire to remain one?

Make no mistake, my movement would have been much more compromised.

As it is, we are now into September, and I have become a ten-times-a-month runner. My target this month is set at twelve times up and down the hill and maybe working towards a double circuit on one day a week. Now, it takes twenty-four minutes up and eighteen minutes down. I have knocked three minutes off my running time for these three and a half miles over these last six months.

Movement is my saving grace.

My subconscious is drawn to this idea of motion. One image that keeps bubbling up on these runs of mine comes from childhood. A day out shopping with my mum. It was December. Still preschool. A Christmas treat. A visit to Chiesmans department store in Lewisham and my first ride on Santa's train, down in the basement.

I was terrified.

'Are you sure you want to do this, Robert?'

My voice said, 'Yes!'

I was on board. Alone. We were off. The excitement was too much. I probably wet myself.

'That's the last time you're going on that thing!'

My mum was embarrassed and angry.

But I had loved it so much. And we had gone so far together, my teddy and me, on that magical train journey to Santaland. We were rocking from side to side in that carriage for hours. Peter Ted and I still talk about it when he decides to join me on one of my runs and hitches a lift on my shoulders.

The author Rob, Peter Ted, and Mum in Lewisham in 1952

Another image of movement arrives. This route of mine, up and down the Trevalgan hill, has become an escalator. I am running on the spot, and it is the road which is moving under my feet. Back to my ride with Peter Ted on the magic Santa train. I am moving even as I remain still. A cunning way to take the sting out of motion.

A tragic bubble now. I remember the discovery I made on my second ascent of this hill back in 2013. When I reached the summit, I decided to stop and explore a National Trust footpath that disappeared away to my right. A short distance along, I came across a plaque fixed in the surface of a granite tor. It was a memorial to Peter Lanyon (1918–1964), the St Ives artist who died in a gliding accident. For some years, I assumed that he had crashed into the top of this very hill but not so. He died in hospital at Taunton in Somerset of injuries received in a gliding accident, miles away from St Ives where he was born.

But his last flight, his final farewell movement, will always be here for me; the scene plays out as I begin each

Peter Lanyon memorial plaque, near the summit of Little Trevalgan

ascent, glancing upwards to that summit moorland. I shut my eyes and open them. In front of me, a memory from four years back. A hawk hangs in the air above me as I race down the upper slope. A honey buzzard, my later research suggests. I would not wish to be a fieldmouse with such a shape hovering in the firmament, fixing me in its sights. The hawk begins its descent, dropping sheer with such grace and intent. A flash of understanding. I am the one under attack!

Hawks must love a bit of fun, too. It peels off inches above my head.

One more image thrusts its way through. Oh! This is very contemporary. The movement of swallows, gliding down with such speed and grace, through the open outer door of my St John's church. Straight into the shelter of the porch where the couple have made a nest in the rafters and hatched their four offspring. Soon, there are six glorious swallows viewed from the marble bench in the church grounds over three wonder-filled weeks. Coming and going, growing strong on their diet of flies before the flight to Africa.

Africa again! Crocosmia and swallows and Libyans – all African migrants. My runner's story is a global story embracing the continents of our planet, Earth. One vital inspiration, remember, lies in New Zealand where Jacinda Ardern, the prime minister, condemned the "unthinkable". Dare we put this into words? Yes! The pursuit of herd immunity as a protection against coronavirus before a vaccine had been developed. Letting the virus run through your population. The unthinkable. Our European and Indian and American reality.

Enough of this reverie. I am running across the start of the road to Trenwin. Time to reach into the magic bole again. I want to share with you what I now know about the movement of a virus one hundred years or so ago.

In 1918, a deadly power oozed across the globe. Back then, our planet was inhabited by 1.8 billion of our species, Homo sapiens. This killing force took out between fifty and one hundred million people, between 2.5 and 5 per cent of the earth's population. Record-keeping varied widely, which is why we will never know the number of lives extinguished before their time.

Back then, they did not even know the nature of the enemy that was infecting them. How can you meaningfully suspect a virus when the notion of a virus is still full of mystery? Coronaviruses were not identified as such by the scientists until the mid-1960s. A Russian botanist, Dmitri Ivanovsky, had in 1892 postulated a virus as the cause of a disease in tobacco plants, but such a virus had to be smaller than any bacteria and impossible to see even under a microscope. No test existed for them. It is estimated that one in three of humankind were visited by this unknown and invisible viral killer. Another decade and more passed before scientists were able to identify the monster responsible for this carnage. We now know it as H1N1, the mother of all pandemics.

Such trauma. I guess that is sufficient reason why I and so many others ended up knowing so little about this planetary event. It remained a footnote to the end of WWI I heard about in passing. All of humanity had been enveloped by the collective sigh of pain.

"Don't go there. Too much grief."

And the outcome of man-made wars still had to be worked through. Seventeen million dead bodies from the WWI (1914–18). Sixty million corpses from WWII (1939–45).

Yet, this tsunami of death by disease in the Spanish flu of 1918 has a claim to be the worst natural disaster to hit humankind. And it can offer us fresh insights into our present pandemic. Let me say that much of what I now know and share with you has come from the pages of a magisterial book by a science journalist. Her name is Laura Spinney and the book is called *Pale Rider – the Spanish Flu of 1918 and how it changed the world* (2017). I love her big picture presentation. In her words, at the root of every pandemic, there is an encounter between a disease-causing microorganism and a human being.

The first wave of this flu pandemic came in April and May 1918 and was relatively mild. The second wave began in August 1918 at three points around the Atlantic: Freetown in Sierra Leone, Boston in the USA and Brest in France. Troop movements were instrumental in its spread. By December, this second wave was virtually over, having covered almost all the planet and proved the deadliest of these viral movements. The third wave struck early in 1919 and, like the first wave, was less lethal. By May 1919, it was over in the northern hemisphere

So much for the chronology. What of the nature of this beast, that came like a thief in the night? At first, the infected knew nothing of their condition. They were, to use the currency that has become familiar in our pandemic, asymptomatic. A period of high infectivity came before the onset of symptoms. Oh! These viruses know a thing or two about maximising their chances of replication.

Then came the cough, the fever, the aches, the dizziness, the insomnia, the loss of hearing, the loss of smell, the blurred vision.

If your card was marked, next came the complications. Bacterial pneumonia arrived. Breathing became laboured. Mahogany spots appeared over cheekbones. In a few hours, the face was flushed with colour "until it is hard to distinguish the coloured men from the white", in the words of one US army doctor. When the redness turned to blue, it was as good as over. Blue turned to black. The extremities first, then up the limbs to cover all. At the age of thirty-eight in November 1918, Guillaume Apollinaire, the avant-garde French poet, "was completely black", according to a friend who saw him dead. Autopsies of victims revealed red, swollen lungs that were congested with haemorrhaged blood, the surface of the lungs covered in a watery pink lather.

In 1918, all a physician could hope to do was keep the patient hydrated and trust that the patient would be nursed well. It was all too much. In time, fatigue set in. The mayor of San Francisco let his mask slip during an Armistice parade in November. People began to complain in the USA about the injustice of churches being shut but stores remaining open. The newspapers kept quiet about the true scale of the pandemic.

For a second, I am back from my bole and feeling so alive. My body is upright and balanced. There is a rhythm to my running. I am feeling fitter. It is a beautiful autumnal day. In the big picture, 102 years is a blink of the eyelid. How little has changed in some respects. There are those who still choose to ignore the power of natural forces to wipe out human beings. Yet, we do know so much more. The enemy has been identified. The most populated state on the planet – China – soon stopped the virus in its tracks with the loss of only four and a half thousand lives. It could have been so, so much more. New Zealand, with the relatively tiny population of 4.9 million, also took the right steps to eliminate the virus and has lost only twenty-five lives. Our killing fields are man-made. They are unnatural.

Back then, in 1918, the death toll was remarkable in its geographical unevenness. Excess mortality rates indicate that if you lived in certain parts of Asia, you were thirty times more likely to die of Spanish flu than if you were a subject or citizen in certain parts of Europe. Asia and Africa took the brunt of the flu slaughter. In India, a reputed jewel in the British imperial crown, between thirteen million and eighteen million died from this viral infection. Cities fared worse than rural areas, but variations within cities were marked. Disparities in wealth and caste, bad diet, slum living conditions, poor access to healthcare, all served to weaken the constitution and hasten the onset of death. An underlying disease made the patient more susceptible to the Spanish flu. Persians serving in the British army in India were more severely affected because they were more likely to be suffering from malaria and its complication, anaemia. The lack of red blood cells – low haemoglobin levels – weakened the immune response to the invasion of the flu virus.

I find that particularly scary. My haemoglobin level is stable but low at 123. Another side effect of my hormonal treatment.

Laura Spinney's account of the 1918 pandemic offers the chilling suggestion that the virus seems to have undergone a small but critical change between the summer and autumn of 1918. Hence the much more virulent nature of the virus by the autumn and winter. We, in 2020, are sitting on a viral timebomb and Johnson is still talking about all this being over by Christmas. Thank goodness, there is still this difference between 1918 and 2020: in 1918, the virus was as lethal in the twenty to forty age range as it was for the elderly; in 2020, that is not the case.

We need to keep our fingers crossed and be prepared.

Halfway down this incline and striding strong. Putting my faith in hope. I trust that Joe Biden will win the US presidential election in November in a couple of months. This 2020 virus is feeding off the likes of Trump in America and Johnson in the UK, Bolsonaro in Brazil and Modi in India. Narcissists are easy meat for the COVID-19 virus.

Mind you, I learned an intriguing fact from Laura Spinney's book which suggests that the terrible human catastrophe of the Spanish flu also played a part in Donald Trump's elevation to the presidency of the United States of America. As capitalism roared into life across the Pond, the US insurance industry was booming. There were so many salesmen working their pitches. When the pandemic struck in 1918, and all those deaths followed, the insurance industry paid out nearly $100 million to the surviving next of kin. Two such beneficiaries were the widow and the son of a German immigrant who had taken out insurance on his life before the pandemic struck. His death left them wealthy. They invested their windfall in property. The immigrant's grandson is Donald Trump.

These viruses weave their mischief in such complex threads.

# 7

---

# VIRAL REVELATIONS

Halfway down this incline and back into my magic bole. In the real world, the calendar records the day as 24<sup>th</sup> September. It is my seventy-second birthday. As far as I know, I have escaped viral infection by SARS-CoV-2.

I am, by nature, curious. We all start that way. I am one of the lucky ones. My curiosity has not been strangled in childhood, or later, by those around me, in family or neighbourhood or places of learning.

I wanted to know more about this disease that has been labelled by scientists as COVID-19. Let me cut to the quick and clear up any confusions you, my reader, may have:

COVID-19 is caused by a virus known as SARS-CoV-2. This is not a flu virus. And it does not have the H and N antigens that are part of the structure of type A pandemic influenza viruses. More on antigens later.

It has taken me a while to get my head straight about these viral matters. I would like to help further your understanding if I can, especially as our government seems keen to preserve our ignorance. I have had two tutors. Laura Spinney was my first guide. From her, I learned, for instance, that a virus is a parasite. It can only survive within another living organism, its host. It is compelled by its nature to invade a host cell. Howard Pue is also my tutor, and I am indebted to him for many of the viral revelations that follow. He has been an American public health veterinarian for over four decades. Many health departments in the USA employ veterinarians in this capacity, since half of the 1500 or so known human pathogens such as viruses and bacteria are zoonotic. They can be transmitted from animals to people.

Howard has taught me that once inside a host cell, the virus by its nature is programmed to hijack the host's DNA, the memory bank of the individual, which it then uses to produce copies of itself. With replication accomplished, the new viral offspring must leave the host cell and find another. They cannot help themselves. Rather like a cancer cell, as I have already discovered.

"Coughs and sneezes spread diseases".

Tiny droplets of mucus are shot through the air carrying the invisible virus. Our monster needs someone within a couple of metres to latch on to. For a virus to spread, humankind must be living close to one another. This we have only been doing for the last twelve thousand years. That is when we stopped being hunter-gatherers and started settling down as farmers. In time, we moved from villages to towns and then cities. The greater our density, the more the so-called "crowd diseases" licked their microlips. The bacterial crew – typhoid, cholera, tuberculosis – had their heydays a plenty. So too, did the viral boys: measles, smallpox, flu, and now COVID-19. 1918 was an outstanding year. The 2020 vintage is rather good too, make no mistake.

Our scientists have learned a great deal about viruses since the great ignorance of 1918.

Birds, especially waterbirds, are generally considered to be an important source of our human influenza viruses. Bird species have acquired a measure of immunity over time from the viruses flowing within them, just as we have learned to coexist with our common cold viruses. But every now and again, a virus from a bird will make it across the species barrier and a new mutant appears on the block. In the city of humanity.

However, many existing and emerging diseases come from natural reservoirs other than birds. Ebola probably came from bats. HIV made the species leap from wild non-human primates. SARS-CoV-2 – our 2020 virus – may have had its origin in bats, too. Often, there is an intermediate host between the reservoir species and we humans. Pangolins could be the go-between for SARS-CoV-2.

We know so much more now. We can stop the viral flows and the bacterial infections. Some countries have succeeded in doing so. In the past, we did not have the knowledge, which is why influenza has been a notorious serial killer.

It was probably a flu epidemic that the historian Livy was writing about when he recorded the huge losses in the Roman imperial armies in 212bc. Similarly, Charlemagne's armies were most likely slaughtered from within, in a 9th century outbreak of influenza. By the 16th century, when Europeans began exploring the world in ships, "crowd diseases" became "imperial diseases". Native Americans, Australians and Pacific Islanders, Africans – untouched by

Caucasian infection up to that point and with no immunity whatsoever – all fell helpless victim to white men's diseases.

So much death from infection. Yet, it was not until the 1930s that scientists began to understand that it was not just due to bacteria: the $19^{th}$ century discovery. There were also invisible entities that could now be identified as viruses at work in these killing fields. A ferret sneezing in a laboratory gave the game away. The researcher caught the flu. From that humble beginning, the complex biology of viral infection began to be revealed.

I glance over the hedgerow close beside me on my right and back to the granite tors on the skyline behind me. We invest such objects of magnitude with emotion. They can inspire us. They may induce fear. Writers may anthropomorphise and imagine them as having lives of their own. What those mounds of stone cannot do is tell us the facts of our existence, in so far as they can be construed at a particular time in our evolution as a species. Only scientists, within the parameters of provisional truth, can do that. So, deep respect and high fives for scientists.

I have already explained that viruses are programmed to replicate within the host cell they have invaded. To that end, they are equipped with their protein structures that are designed to lock into receptors on the host cell's surface. Imagine a scene from a movie with a manned space capsule docking with the mothership. Only this time, the capsule is manned by space pirates.

Of course, our bodies are not without defence systems. When a human is under viral attack, his or her immune cells secrete tiny morsels of protein called antibodies that attach themselves to the virus, disabling it, if we are lucky. These antibodies may linger in the blood for years and continue to give us a measure of protection but only against the type of virus first encountered. Flu viruses are cunning. They mutate. Influenza viruses come in different varieties, anyway, with four types now identified: A, B, C and D. Only type A causes pandemics. Then, within these types, due to the inherent instability of viruses, the further mutations occur.

If our immune system fails and the defences are breached, the virus now finds itself inside the cell. Once the first task – the hijacking of the host cell's DNA – is accomplished and the virus begins replicating itself, the second task is to break out. A pathway must be opened for the viral offspring to exit, leaving the host cell as dead meat.

The road is now clear for the infection of new cells. In the case of influenza viruses and SARS-CoV-2, that work is focused on the lining of the respiratory tract. The death of the host cells leaves a telltale trail of visible damage inside the body. Our flu and COVID-19 symptoms reveal the consequences to the world outside.

These insights are leaving me with an adrenalin rush. Or is it a hot flush from my hormonal treatment? It is so thrilling to discover such inner secrets of the body. My stride quickens a fraction. Should I become excited by such death-shaped knowledge? That feels much the same dilemma as finding stimulation in Cornish mining history.

The shape of the lay-by at the foot of this incline is becoming clearer.

My birthday circuit run.

This feels a small miracle. Above me, the storm clouds gather and there is mizzle in the air. Four days ago, last Sunday, I emerged through the low granite archway that leads up from the church grounds. Ella, our bearded collie, led the way on her lead. I leaned forwards and the muscle spasm in the lower back told me the bad news. I was now fit only for a period of rest and self-manipulation.

Yet, our bodies are such amazing creations! Oh – let us praise their powers of recovery! I have been here so often in the past forty years, mending from lower back injury. Ever since that nun, in full habit from the convent in Brent, drove into the side of my car on the roundabout near Aylestone school as I returned home in the autumn of 1978. Or perhaps I should track the original source of the injury back to the fatal car crash in Slough on 10th March 1974.

'Mea culpa! I really should have stopped.'

Her words. Not mine.

Sister Whip Lash.

Back then in 1978, the ache in the lower back got worse and worse as the end of term grew nearer. I woke up on the first day of the Christmas vacation in tears with pain. By the end of the afternoon, I was lying in a hospital bed. Two months later – it was the winter of discontent, the prelude to Maggie Thatcher's landslide election victory in 1979 – the surgeon had performed his operation. I had a laminectomy to add to my medical records. A defenestration to the disc. And wonder of wonders, I could walk again.

Once we were under the full throttle of Thatcherism, my times of spasm began. They have never fully gone away. The movement into running started in the mid-1980s. It was my bid to keep fit and oil this body of mine. Keeping the pains at bay. In the circumstances, my effort has enjoyed remarkable success. Four marathons under my belt since 2012. Thank you again, Ben and Tanya, my current physio team. This week, though, it has just been me, working on the foundations they have helped lay. And I mend fast. Hence, the joy of this running experience today.

Mind you, it did help getting the results of my latest three-monthly blood test a couple of days ago. Testosterone still untraceable. And my haemoglobin level up six points at 129. Only four more points needed to reach the normal range of 133–167. The daily iron tablets are working well, mixed with my local running.

I hope you do not think me too obsessed with such bodily matters. I cannot help myself. I am fascinated by this extraordinary frame that has been designed to coat the soul, the life force, call it what you will. No, I am not slipping into a Cartesian fallacy. The body cannot be separated from the mind. But neither term – body nor mind – are quite sufficient to the task. We need a sense of both to approach an understanding of who and what we are.

How I love this facility of expressing thoughts for you to catch. If you care enough to. There is so much interference in the way these days. You may not wish to share all my fury at our misgovernment, at least, not yet. But I hope you do choose to learn a thing or two about this monster in our midst.

In 1931, the first virus was grown in a fertilised chicken's egg by two American pathologists, Alice Woodruff and Ernest Goodpasture. They had observed that chicken eggs could become infected by a disease of poultry called fowl pox that is caused by a virus. Now, the road was clear for the development of vaccines to target viruses. In 1936, the first flu vaccine was produced by a Russian, A. A. Smorodintseff. He took a flu virus and grew it in an egg. Then, he extracted those offspring of the virus that seemed the weakest, the ones replicating the least well, and grew them in another egg. He repeated this process thirty times until he had a virus that was scarcely able to replicate at all. And this weakened virus then became the vaccine that left the first human guinea pigs with a tiny touch of fever and immunity from reinfection with flu. At least, for that strain of flu.

I am in awe of Smorodintseff and his brilliance. I almost wish I had followed the sciences at school and not the arts. More than a billion Russians, mostly factory workers, received such vaccines as a defence against type A influenza – the pandemic variety – over the next fifty years, until the collapse of the Soviet Union. By 1944, the American troops arriving in the European battle grounds were subject to mass flu vaccination that provided protection against a variety of flu viruses. A year earlier, in 1943, the flu virus was seen for the first time, thanks to the invention of the electron microscope.

What does it look like? Spherical, in shape. A core of genetic information surrounded by a protein layer and sealed within a covering whose surface is coated with what look like lollipops. These are different types of proteins, which induce an immune response in the host body. We humans have such a smart design. Our immune systems recognise these proteins as foreign invaders and produce antibodies to stop the invasion. So, these proteins are antibody generators, otherwise known as "antigens", for short. Dire news for the virus. Destroyed by its own lollipops.

However, these surface proteins are far from being blanket bad news for the virus. Viruses have their own uses for them. In type A influenza viruses – pandemic killers such as Spanish flu – there are two important, and prominent, proteins on the surface of the virus which scientists have named H (haemagglutinin) and N (neuraminidase). Extra big lollipops. The virus employs H as its sledgehammer to break into the host cell. N is used as the cutting tool to open the way for the release of the viral offspring after replication.

All this is breathtaking. I now know that viruses use their proteins for their own selfish purposes at our expense, whilst we use the antigenic properties of these proteins to protect ourselves. Our bodies generate antibodies, as we have seen, and our scientists use the antigenic properties of H and N to develop specific flu vaccines to prevent infection in the first place. What a battlefield!

Having reached into the bole to locate these gems of science, I would like to stay inside this magic interlude a little longer to explain why the vaccine to protect against COVID-19, when it does arrive in our drive-in surgeries, is likely to be one that must be given afresh every year. We may well be living with COVID jabs for the rest of our lives.

The fact that we are a product of our DNA (deoxyribonucleic acid) and our environment is scientific knowledge that has generally soaked into our consciousness, although we may not understand too much about what that really means. No matter. We may even have picked up on the fact that DNA is a double-stranded helix.

Now for something I did not know. The genetic material in most viruses is usually made up of single-stranded RNA (ribonucleic acid), not our double-stranded DNA. Now, critically, RNA is less stable than DNA. Therefore, errors are more frequent in replication, which mean that viruses take different forms over time. Such mutations are good news for viruses. They help ensure their survival and potency. Their ability to infect human cells is enhanced. Their resistance to anti-viral drugs is improved. These new forms of virus mean new viral subtypes. That is why the vaccine in our annual flu jab must be formulated afresh every year.

The 1918 Spanish flu virus, which took at least fifty million lives, is now known as subtype H1N1. The 1957 Asian flu virus, that slaughtered approaching two million, was identified as subtype H2N2. The 1968 Hong Kong flu virus, which took up to four million lives, was labelled as subtype H3N2. A flu pandemic in 2009, responsible for the death of as many as a half a million, was due to a virus named as subtype (H1N1)pdm09. The annual influenza vaccine that has been produced every year since then, including 2020, has included a strain of this 2009 viral subtype. It is at work inside my body right now and Louise's. We are following the science for real.

Time now, to consider our present viral pandemic. We have become used to talking about our 2020 virus as a coronavirus. I wanted to know more about this parasite. The first human coronavirus was not discovered and identified until 1965. Coronaviruses (CoV) are a large family of viruses, some of which can be transmitted from animals to people. They are the cause of illnesses such as Middle East respiratory syndrome (MERS) and COVID-19. Our COVID-19 virus is so-called because it is a coronavirus disease (hence COVID) that was first discovered in 2019. In short, an infectious acute respiratory disease caused by a novel coronavirus. "Corona" is Latin for "crown". In addition to appearing like a solar corona or halo, this virus has a crown-like appearance.

SARS-CoV-2 virus, photographed by
Radoslav Zilinsky and licensed by Getty Images

Time for a reminder, I think. We are dealing with a killer virus. In March of this year, it was the case that globally, about 3.4 per cent of reported COVID-19 cases had died. The World Health Organisation updated this figure on 19th October 2020. There are now nearly forty million confirmed cases, with 1,111,998 deaths – a 2.8 per cent mortality rate. Round up or round down, that is around a three per cent mortality. By comparison, much less than one per cent of those infected die from seasonal flu. But, of course, mortality rates are largely determined by access to healthcare and pre-existing medical conditions. For COVID-19, data to date suggest that eighty per cent of infections are mild or asymptomatic. Most of the other twenty per cent are severe infections that will lead to a bed in hospital, if there is a healthcare system in place to provide one. Three quarters of these cases are severe infections, requiring oxygen, and a quarter are critical, needing ventilation. Within this last critical group, over half the patients will die.

I am so relieved that my haemoglobin score has only four points to climb to reach the normal range. I need my defences to be in full working order. When a virus invades, the body's immune system bursts into action. Within minutes, a substance called interferon is secreted by several kinds of cells in the infected host. Interferon is a protein that acts rather like a railway signalling system, in that it alerts infected and nearby uninfected cells that an invader is at hand, and they need to activate their immune responses. The alert goes out to all traffic. There is an unscheduled freight train on the line, and it is loaded with high explosives. But the cunning virus has evolved to conceal the evidence that it is within microseconds of bursting into the host cell, and sometimes it succeeds in blocking the communications network.

How amazing it is that we should be a decade away from planetary catastrophe due to the selfishness and greed of a few, whilst our scientists over the last century and more have revealed such wonders at work inside our bodies, for good and ill. We know so much more than we ever have done, yet we are so close to our own destruction.

Back to the magic bole and more about these interferons that are so-called because their purpose in life is to "interfere" with viral replication. They are the good guys and belong to a large class of proteins known as cytokines. Within the amazingly complex cascade of events that medical scientists are beginning to unravel, these cytokine molecules play a critical part in the communication between cells which trigger the protective defences of the immune system in the battle against pathogens such as viruses. The freight train with its deadly load is targeted.

Virologists have also identified specialised white blood cells in our immune system and named them as macrophages, from the Greek for large eaters (gluttons in short). These macrophages are designed to help hunt down the bacteria and viruses. They are responsible for initiating that remarkably complex sequence that leads to the production of cytokines.

They are also destroyers. They gobble up the enemy. Hence their name. Macrophages engulf and digest cellular debris and any foreign substance that does not pass the healthy protein test. That unscheduled deadly freight train disappears in a microsecond. But their appetite is ravenous. They cannot get enough of the unhealthy stuff.

Almost at the lay-by now. The pavement begins on the right-hand side of the road in forty yards or so. I have loved discovering these viral secrets. I hope all you who are catching the drift of everything I am sharing with you do, too. One of the calumnies directed at young people today is that they have a reduced attention span. I have always been on the side of those generations that were born after the baby boomers, my generation, so I hope there is little truth in that generalisation. If any of you, whatever your age, find your eyes have glazed over when confronted with the wonders of medical science, ponder these facts about the "cytokine storm".

The cytokines produced by the macrophages work to increase the blood flow to tissues affected by the viral invasion. In this way, more immune cells can reach the battleground. The reason why the 1918–19 pandemic had a much higher mortality rate than the deadly pandemics of more recent times is that in the second wave – in the autumn and winter of 1918 – those most affected were in the twenty-to-forty-year-old age group. How come? These guys were the fittest. Their immune systems were so resilient that they went into supercharged overdrive. The macrophage and cytokine cellular microdance, that is designed by nature to provide immunity to the body, went rogue. The outcome was evident in the redness and swelling, the inflammation around the infected area. Conduct an autopsy and the evidence is clear. Witness the effects of a cytokine storm. The more aggressive the tempest, the harder it is to resist death.

Any of you younger and fitter than me, beware. Read the writing on the medical scientist's wall. Observing safe distancing above all, and hand washing and wearing masks, will be life-preserving advice during each one of the three waves usually associated with viral pandemics. We should all be keeping our fingers crossed that the pattern evident in the 1918–19 second wave is not repeated in 2020–21.

I did not know any of this medical science before COVID-19 arrived and I started my run. How much of all this do the politicians who pull the levers of power in countries across the world know now? Do they grasp what they are up against? The Chinese learned fast. So too, did New Zealanders. Yet, so much of the rest of the world has put the pursuit of profit before the defence of lives. Such immeasurable stupidity. We are left with both the killing fields and our economies ruined.

# 8

---

# DEATH TOLLS AND
# INTERCONNECTIONS

Reaching the lay-by is always a feel-good moment. Ahead of me is the pavement. I am back in urban St Ives. The trappings of the town are unfolding before me. Time to see what more my magic bole has to offer. I am at peace with myself and at one with my body, whatever is revealed and despite the current circumstances.

Do you remember I was looking forward to completing a double circuit of this run of mine in September? It did not happen. But in this month, in late October, I have run double circuits of seven miles the last two Sunday mornings. Decent times on the TomTom, too. Around one hour and twenty-seven minutes on both occasions.

Usually, I would be at church on a Sunday morning. I did attend for a sequence of twelve weeks through the summer when the services were held in the open air outside the church. However, with winter approaching, our vicar has put up a marquee in the vicarage garden where the faithful can gather and celebrate. Louise and I do not feel safe attending. It seems acts of worship are exempt from the rule that no more than six people may gather. We cannot see the reasoning behind that.

The second wave of COVID-19 has closed in over our land. On Tuesday, 20 October 2020, the daily death toll from the SARS-CoV-2 virus was 241, the highest since early June. 21,300 new cases were recorded on that day, with hotspots in north-west and north-east England, the east Midlands and parts of Yorkshire. Class conflict is becoming more visible. Andy Burnham, the Labour mayor of Greater Manchester, has accused Boris Johnson of "grinding communities into the ground" and "playing poker with people's lives" after the prime minister refused to grant all the extra cash the city needed to support the lowest paid workers who had lost their jobs due to the tightening of restrictions.

As this fresh surge of death sweeps over us, I grow ever more mindful of the importance and power of interconnections in our life stories. On these runs of mine, when I reflect upon my own life, I realise how I have created a meaning for my existence through various narrative threads that link people I know and have known with events in my own life and the world around me. This is my own experiential tapestry, always open, I hope, to the possibility of redesigning, but at any one moment the embodiment of all the interconnections made during my lifetime.

Death severs interconnections. When I see and hear the daily bulletins on *Channel 4 News* of the rising number of deaths laid at the door of COVID-19, I fume. On Tuesday, 27 October 2020, the death toll from COVID-19 was given as 43,400. All these are lives cut short. Hopes unrealised, connections unmade, human touches not exchanged. I grieve for these souls that are lost. Victims of the actions and inactions of those who should be charged, at the very least, with corporate manslaughter.

But what of the missing dead? There are still more lost souls to grieve for. Twenty thousand at least. How dare they be dismissed from public knowledge through statistical conjuring tricks. As if they never existed. Think of all the interconnections they would have made if their lives had not been cut short. And now to suffer this double cut. Removed from the ranks of the living and then erased from the already grim figures.

In the summer of 2020, the government of Johnson and Cummings changed the definition of a COVID-19 death in England. It had been all deaths after a positive test. Now it became those deaths within twenty-eight days of recorded infection. At a stroke, the UK's nominally official death toll fell by 5,377 (sixteen per cent), from 42,072 to 36,695. Where were the cries of outrage at this gerrymandering of the statistics? The mainstream media and politicians hardly muttered a word in protest.

But even this blatant manipulation is less significant than the refusal to use the excess mortality rates based on death certification data to calculate the human cost of this pandemic. These are the figures that have the approval of the international scientific and medical communities. These are the statistics that historians in the future will be using to record the death toll from COVID-19.

That is why I am bringing the future forwards. From the online site of the *British Medical Journal*, I have found that in the five months between March and July this year, there were fifty-eight thousand such excess deaths in England and Wales. Officially, fifty-two thousand (eighty-nine per cent) were related to COVID-19. The chances are that a good number of those six thousand non-COVID-19 deaths were in fact associated with the disease but were not registered as such. We are, after all, living through a pandemic. And too many are dying in its wake.

And remember – this land of ours is, for the time being, the United Kingdom. What of the excess deaths between March and July in Scotland and Northern Ireland? My Google search for the figures for Scotland was hampered by the way the data was presented. I had to make an estimate for deaths in hospital from COVID-19. But I ended up with a Scottish mortality total of 7,715. It is difficult to resist the conclusion that the Scottish government statisticians were under orders not to reveal that awful fact.

My search for the figures for excess deaths in Northern Ireland was more straightforward, although they cover only the four-month period between March and June. There were 885 excess deaths within those months, of which 837 (ninety-five per cent) were recorded as deaths due to COVID-19.

Combine the figures for excess deaths in all the nations of the United Kingdom and we reach a total of around 66,600.

And that is just in the first wave. RIP all of you who are the hearts and souls in those statistics. And heaven help us in this second wave.

Can you understand now why I fume when I see and hear the falsified figures on *Channel 4 News* of deaths from COVID-19? All mainstream media follow the same pattern of under-recording. *Channel 4* is not alone.

As we approach November, some medical scientists are concluding that almost one hundred thousand people a day are becoming infected. May Heaven forbid! Even taking a mortality rate of two per cent, that means that by the end of November, there will be around two thousand British citizens dying as each day passes. What can we do now to stop the sweep of the Grim Reaper's scythe? The action the government should take – and did take so belatedly in March this year – is lock down the nation. But it is not doing so. And each day that passes will cost so many more lives in a month's time. Such dying is not in the natural order. We must rage against this abomination.

And this government of which I speak, what is it? No more and no less than two men. Johnson and Cummings. How has it come to this? What are the interconnections in the lives of men and women over time and space that can explain this horror show? How have we ended up in thrall to those who should be held responsible for the crisis in the first place?

Over the Channel, in Europe, President Macron in France is announcing a new national lockdown and Angela Merkel in Germany is on the brink of doing so, too. Here, the leader who has swathed himself in quasi-presidential powers is saying nothing of substance and allowing the hopeless, mad pursuit of herd immunity to continue.

Time to pay tribute to one victim of this madness. He is Dr Abdul Mabud Chowdhury. Interconnections have made this man the centre of my thoughts. I happened to watch a news feature about him that caught my attention. Commemorating him like this is my way of paying tribute to a remarkable man who symbolises for me the worth of all those other lives lost through misgovernment. Specifically, nearly two hundred frontline health and care workers who have died after contracting coronavirus. BAME staff account for sixty per cent of NHS staff deaths.

Abdul Mabud Chowdhury – a consultant urologist at Homerton hospital in Hackney in East London – died on Wednesday, 8 April this year from the coronavirus. He was fifty-three and had no underlying health conditions. A week before he fell ill, he wrote a Facebook message to Boris Johnson in which he urged him to ensure that frontline NHS staff had the PPE they needed. *Healthcare workers*, he wrote, *are in direct contact with patients* and have a *human right like others to live in this world disease-free with our family and children.* I remember his grieving son being so proud of him. We all should be.

Interconnections are filling my head. His name sounds the same as the doctor who cared for me and my parents when we were ill during my childhood. My doctor's name was Chaudhuri. Dr Chaudhuri was a strange but kindly figure who held court in a shabby, small surgery with strange smells and a dozen metal chairs in the waiting room. Since I only saw him when I was ill, he remained rather unknown.

And I was puzzled. I could not work out why he was liked and respected by my father when my dad was rude about other people who were not white like himself. I remember being curious enough to ask a question about this mystery. My father thought for a moment. 'Dr Chaudhuri is like Kanwal, my Indian batman. A good man, a civilised man.'

My dad had even given me Kanwal as my third forename as a mark of respect for his Indian subject. Two Christian names and a Hindu forename. A fine way to set you up for life.

Robert Eric Kanwal Donovan. I have no idea where the Eric came from. But I remember the sinking feeling in the depths of my being when the teacher read out my name in the rollcall before class in my first year at grammar school. Donovan, Robert Eric Kanwal. R.E.K. The class joker leapt at the opportunity.

'Wreck!'

I lived with the humiliation of being called "Wreck" for nearly a year, until I became a second-former and was gifted the means to transform the insult to a kinder language where I became simply "REK" – a boy who had been seen to pass muster.

My gym master, Mike Richardson (the names of heroes remain etched in the memory for a lifetime), had organised a series of boxing lessons that saw us equipped with boxing gloves and taught the basics of the noble art. We were then paired with others of a similar ability for three one-minute rounds of combat. No blows to the head. No blows below the belt. Mr Richardson reserved the right to call time early.

I got Minter as my opponent. Oh, the anger that surged through me. Minter (please forgive me, Mr Minter, wherever you are) had suffered the same kind of taunting that I had been subjected to as "Wreck", in his case because of his size. He was small. This matching was so wrong. I would not be shamed in this way. I came out from my corner and thumped my way through into his body. My blows tore into him. It lasted less than forty-five seconds. Mr Richardson stopped the fight, looked round and picked a new opponent for me.

'Right, Donovan – three rounds with Clarke.' Oh, Mike, you just gifted me manna from heaven. Johnny Clarke was thirteen years old. I am sure his puberty started years earlier.

He was already shaving. They said he had a girlfriend. And you should have heard the dirty stories he repeated in the metalwork class, having heard them from his dad. Johnny was from the wrong side of the tracks in Dartford, the working-class lad who was doubly gifted being both clever in class and a natural sportsman. We all looked up to Johnny.

Our class of over twenty little boys surrounded Johnny and me in the makeshift ring. They had just watched my thrashing of Minter. That was a turn-up. 'We did not expect that,' their collective unspoken voice. Now, they waited with bated breath to see Clarke demolish Donovan. Only he did not. Round one passed and Donovan was still trading blows. Clarke seemed puzzled. This was unexpected. Round two came to an end and Donovan was still on his feet, still trying to throw punches. Round three was one of the longest minutes of my life. Please, please, Mr Richardson, do not bring this to an end. Not until the minute is up.

Please.

In my head, the guardian angels were chanting:

*Keep punching.*

*Keep punching.*

*Keep punching.*

I could barely hold my arms up I was so weak.

And then came the bell, and the rest of my life as REK Donovan began.

Another critical link in the chain of my being had been forged in those three minutes of mortal combat. The interconnections that were to lead to an exit from that school as an Oxford scholar, an Alan Bennett history boy, had received a God almighty boost. My sense of self had started to blossom.

Interconnections matter. They provide the stuff of the meanings we bring to life. But there is nothing inevitable about the welding of these links. Yet once they are formed, these chains of meaning that we meld have substance. There may be elements of myth within them, but all myths contain truths about what it is to be human. That is what I believe. That is part of my philosophy of life.

The connections I have traced in this chapter have such substance. When death strikes, there is a gap. Substance is lost. The possibility of moulding more connections fades. For the person who is no longer alive, the human performance is over. But the loss is wider still. The body that is wheeled away to the mortuary en route to the crematorium or graveyard serves as a reminder of all the interconnections that will now never be forged. There is loss here for the family and for the community who knew this living being. There is also loss for the wider society who never knew this departed soul.

John Donne was teasing out this awesome truth towards the end of 1623 as he recovered from an illness that could have taken his life. He, like others then, knew the reality of death far more intimately than most of us do. He had lost a wife and children. As he wrote, around him London was in the grip of an unknown disease producing rashes and fevers in its victims and leading to death for many. Death was around the corner back then in a way that we in the protected cocoon of our advanced industrialised society find difficult to imagine. Yet still, Donne was able to reach out and prize the worth of every single soul in this sea of mortality. Here he is, in these words from his *Meditation XVII*, a link in a chain of profound insight that stretches across time:

*No man is an Island, entire of itself; every man is a piece of the Continent, a part of the main... any man's death diminishes me, because I am involved in Mankind; And therefore never send to know for whom the bell tolls; It tolls for thee.*

Anyone's death diminishes me. I am grieving for all the links that have been lost to COVID-19. A viral pandemic that could and should have been averted.

# 9

## PAVEMENT MATTERS

The first thought I have as I feel the pavement beneath my feet is *don't trip up*. There is a paradox for you. I pound the surface of the road, dodging the occasional pothole as I run up and down the steep gradients of this hill, and remain stable and fearless. I switch to the asphalt of the pavement, as the terrain becomes more level, and my insecurities about balance flood in.

But just look at what I can see in front of me. Months of lockdown this year have led to the timetables for highway maintenance being torn to shreds. Tufts of green grass, rooted in the gutter of the road, spill over and onto the pavement. The edge of the kerb is concealed. One clumsy placing of my stride, my ankle twists, and I would be over. On the other side of this already narrow pavement, autumnal brown ferns, prickly brambles, stinging nettles and more grass encroach from the hedge's base.

I glimpse a metaphor for the breakdown of society.

Sometimes, I choose to continue running in the road.

It feels safer. Besides, the flow of my runner's thoughts can vanish when faced with the challenge of judging the strides on the pavement. But there are other times when my guardian angels just sweep me along. I find myself now at the end of this ill-maintained stretch, not far from the entrance to Hellesveor farm, a cluster of barns in a sea of mud, soundtracked by the barks of a deep-throated guard dog. And I have no conscious memory of having navigated my way through these pavement minefields. My train of thought has taken over.

Whether it be on the risk-filled pavement or the road, I sense that this run of mine is entering its final stages. Time for taking stock. Time, in a moment, for more fruits from the magic bole.

I have a sense of loss. My entry into an urban landscape means I have lost the wide vistas of my hill sections. My spirit feels cramped. I am excited by the thought of being closer to the completion of the run, but I am pining for those views and the perspectives they gave me. Some days are like this. Living through a pandemic in a country that is being misgoverned is no joyride. The green stuff of hope can be harder to grasp, however much you try.

We are now approaching mid-November in this dismal land which is sinking ever further into the morass shaped by the misgovernment of Johnson and Cummings. So much is going wrong for Boris Johnson. Or at least you would think it should be. But in a land at war, gripped by an embedded fear of a deadly enemy, many of its people cling to their leader in a spirit of trust. There is a deeply rooted need for those at the top to be doing their best and getting it as right as they possibly can. Our leaders know this. They repeat the mantra that everyone is working twenty-fours a day and doing everything humanly possible to get things back to normal. This virus will be defeated. Whatever it takes.

Only they are failing. Miserably.

It is true that Johnson has been forced into what he called another national lockdown, starting on Thursday, 5 November 2020 and scheduled to remain in place for a month until 2nd December. Faced with a daily death toll forecast at over one thousand, he and Cummings knew their mortuary planning would be overwhelmed. The iconic NHS is facing imminent collapse. People have once more been told to stay at home. Non-essential shops and venues are instructed to close.

But schools, colleges and universities will remain open. Such madness. The education sector is responsible for thirty-four per cent of viral infection. This is wilful bad government, following a policy that will lead to yet more body bags. Five weeks and more of criminal neglect underpin this awful scenario.

This latest national lockdown arrived a week or so after Johnson had announced, on 23rd October, a three-tier system of restrictions across the country which, predictably, failed to stop the exponential rise in infections and deaths. A couple of hours after Boris Johnson donned his leader's mantle to announce the intricate measures of this tiered system, the minutes of a SAGE meeting from 21st September were released. These showed that the members of SAGE were so worried about the rise in COVID-19 infections, they were calling for a short "circuit breaker" form of national lockdown. It does not take a science degree to recognise the self-evident truth of this minute:

*The more rapidly interventions are put in place, and the more stringent they are, the faster the reduction in incidence and prevalence and the greater the reduction in COVID-related deaths.*

The SAGE group also noted that the Test and Trace system, once heralded as "world-beating" by Boris Johnson, was *only having a marginal impact on controlling the virus*. So much for the failure by late September to "test, test and test", as urged by the WHO. It gets worse. By the beginning of November, the NHS COVID-19 app, downloaded by nineteen million citizens of the United Kingdom, was found to have been set at the wrong sensitivity. For a month, the Department of Health and Social Care had failed to use software developed to make the app work properly. As a result, thousands of users who should have received an alert to self-isolate were not contacted. The media and the politicians barely blinked at this news. Accountability has gone out of the window. No heads roll. No one falls on their sword.

It would have come as no surprise to those few who knew that, back in September, the prime minister chose to ignore his scientific advisors and pander to those voices within his own party who were pressing to keep the economy running, whatever the cost. After all, that was the approach he and Cummings had chosen as their response to the coronavirus in February. The adoption of the "unthinkable", as Jacinda Ardern in New Zealand called it. Chasing the dragon of herd immunity. After months of repetition of the mantra, "we are following the science in everything we do", Johnson stopped even pretending to do so.

We have no need to wait on scientific advisors or prime

ministers to tell us that dramatically rising infection rates will lead to blood-chilling mortality figures. Just remember, and use the 2.8 per cent rule, or round down to two per cent to take account of hope. When 33,470 people are reported as confirmed COVID-19 cases, as they were on Thursday, 12 November, it means that a month or so later there will be around 670 lifeless bodies. In fact, the death toll is likely to be even higher since there will be those who have the virus but are untested and undiagnosed.

And if the daily death toll is given as 563, as it was on that same day, you can work out that around 28,150 people were infected four weeks before. This is a second wave that has been allowed to run out of control, due to five weeks of inadequate oversight. Professor John Edmunds told a parliamentary committee in that third week in October: "There's no way we come out of this [second] wave now without counting our deaths in the tens of thousands."

Are we exceptional in this national madness? Sadly not. Across the pond, the American misgovernment of Trump has led to similar fatal outcomes. Around a quarter-million deaths so far. Yet over the Channel in Europe, Germany, under the leadership of Angela Merkel, has been markedly more successful in controlling the virus. There, an effective Test and Trace system has been established. There, the government is used to spending a much higher proportion of its annual budget on health. There, a well-funded and respected system of local government includes an efficient structure of around four hundred local health authorities.

Here in the UK, local knowledge and understanding of needs have been rejected in favour of centralised planning that has failed time and time again. The use of private enterprise agencies by government departments has also been exposed as ineffective and hugely costly. Strong whiffs of cronyism, and maybe corruption, fill the air. The National Audit Office reported that £10.5 billion of contracts for PPE to NHS and social care institutions had been handed out without competition and those with political connections were ten times more likely to get a deal.

Not all I draw out from the magic bole is soaked in this sorry mix of ineptitude, greed and self-deception that is allowing institutional manslaughter on an industrial scale. Across the Atlantic, in the USA, the forces of darkness have suffered a setback. Donald Trump lost the presidential election at the beginning of November, despite his mad claims to the contrary. Joe Biden will be the president, come 20th January next year; Kamala Harris will be the vice president. He is sane and measured. She too, and an American with a Jamaican father and south Indian mother. The Black Lives Matter movement has received a massive boost on at least two fronts. The wicked racist showman in the White House has had his marching orders and the new vice president will be a woman of colour. A woman, note. Feminism triumphs, too. Two glass ceilings have been shattered.

And what did the prime minister here make of events across the pond? Tellingly, the message of congratulations sent by Boris Johnson to the president-elect was revealed to have had Trump's name underneath Biden's. Boris had backed the wrong horse and will now be seriously anxious. Britain's Trump clone has lost his master and model. Both Johnson and Trump have a narcissistic belief that it is their destiny to lead a nation. And a belief they are superbly equipped to do so by dint of their special genius.

Yet Johnson is by now running on borrowed time. In early November, Dominic Cummings staged a walkout from No.10 after a row with the PM, and a few days later, Boris Johnson was self-isolating after his app alerted him to having had contact with a MP infected with COVID-19. Real news or smoke and mirrors stuff? That is one of the tragedies of the here and now. Trust has been lost. Mistrust becomes a default position. It has for me.

Whatever the bluster, the harsh facts speak for themselves. The UK government has floundered and failed in this war with COVID-19. Johnson still sees himself as a Winston Churchill war-winning figure but he, like Trump, is afflicted with narcissistic personality disorder. Prior to this pandemic, a group of around fifty wealthy Tory backbenchers in parliament, with a mindset shaped by a foolish fantasy in which Britain rediscovers its greatness by leaving Europe, adopted Johnson as their populist tool to bamboozle the voters into voting Tory. "Get Brexit done" was a rallying cry that worked wonders. But now, those same Tory MPs are doubting the merits of their choice.

Jacob Rees Mogg is a leading figure within their ranks. Johnson has made him Leader of the House of Commons. They share an Eton and Oxford education. They are both millionaires. Rees-Mogg worked hard to help get Johnson elected as the leader of the Conservative Party, and so the prime minister, in July 2019. Johnson has few firm beliefs and follows the path that suits his ambitions, but Rees-Mogg and his group share a conviction that Britain really will be great again as a stand-alone power in the world. To that end, markets must be kept open at all costs. The end justifies the means. They are soaked in the spirit of neoliberalism.

Boris Johnson was the chosen tool of these Tory neoliberals, but now they are recalculating. They are looking around to find a safe choice to further their interests when they tell Mr Johnson his time is up. I can hear their whispers.

He is minding too much now about those body bags for our liking. His idle nature has got the better of him. He is too reliant on that special advisor. Dominic Cummings had his Brexit uses. He performed well enough in pursuing herd immunity. But the arrogant little rat has dared show his contempt for the likes of us. Good riddance if he really does intend to stop advising the PM after Christmas. A no-deal Brexit will be in the bag by then. All the easier to perform the last rites for Boris, a leader past his expiry date.

I surface from this reverie. The farm at Hellesveor is getting even nearer. I have, it seems, chosen the pavement path along this stretch. I must take responsibility for my steps now. My guardian angels can rest a while. A familiar smell drifts in my direction on the breeze. The odour is resonant of agribusiness. Roll back to the years of my early childhood and the pong would have been different. Sweeter. More natural.

What, I wonder, would the makers of sweet smells – the hyperosmia, the "super smellers", with their nose for olfactory variations – make of the odours emanating from our political landscape during this pandemic? What variations could they detect in the range before their noses? How much more pungent is the smell of death from, say, bullshit or bluster? Does amused contempt for the gullibility of the population at large have its own special fragrance?

If I glance to the right before I move past Hellesveor farm to my left, I catch sight of the old mill pond in its grounds. By

Running past Hellesveor Farm, with the top
of the church tower visible behind the farm

tradition, every year on Good Friday, children and parents gather around the perimeter with their model boats and the surface of the pond, cleared of reeds, becomes a miniature marina. Wonderful memories for kids to take into their adult life. I have seen the line of parked cars stretch a long way back up the hill from the pavement entrance to the pond. This year, in 2020, there was no regatta due to lockdown. Today, on this mid-November run, the rain has become a drizzle, and as I glimpse the scene, my pond of childhood dreams appears stagnant and diminished. Another metaphor for the present time.

These Brexiteers in parliament are also the advocates of herd immunity. As such, they have left me, and others, burdened. Struggling to hold on to hope. The excess death figure will be approaching one hundred thousand by the time

Running past the old mill pond in Hellesveor

this second wave has had its fill. I hear Hull has become the city with the highest rate of infection in the United Kingdom. Locals are screaming: "Close the schools!". Kids should be the stuff of hope and dreams. Not infection.

Down here, I miss those vistas which graced my running up above. One comes to mind now, not shared before. I understand the reason for my reticence. There is, to my left, as I force my way up the steepest part of the hill, heading for the summit, a cluster of granite outcrops wedged into the moorland slopes. They have such age and power. It is as if a colossal ogre has hammered them in, a creature bent on terrible violence, towering above the scene. One piece of these granite slabs stands out from the others. It must be my height four times over and the width of three of me. Truly, this is the rock of Sisyphus.

Do you remember the myth from ancient Greece? Albert Camus, the French philosopher, was drawn to this story of a king, Sisyphus, who dared cheating death only to be punished by the gods and compelled to push a rock up a mountain to the summit. Then watch it roll down to the bottom. And compelled to repeat the action, again and again and again. Forever.

Camus published his essay *The Myth of Sisyphus* in 1942 as France lay occupied by Nazi Germany. For Camus, the toil of Sisyphus was a metaphor for lives shaped by the relentless rhythm of factory life. Sisyphus, however, is transformed into a hero even as he lives out his absurd and futile task. He is graced to know his own tragedy as he moves down the mountain to start all over again. It is not hope that saves him, though. It is scorn.

*There is no fate that cannot be surmounted by scorn.*

Camus concludes that all will be well. One must imagine that Sisyphus has found contentment in accepting the absurdity of his fate.

I am not prepared to settle for this: a life that has been shrivelled to absurdity. I will not relinquish my belief in the green stuff. Yes, that huge slab of granite on the hillside makes me very afraid. This nightmare of misgovernment and these killing fields are the essence of absurdity. But scorn alone is not enough.

In the face of the challenge of absurdity, I become the prophet again. Always the champion of hope. We can, together, act to change the billing at the magic theatre. The boulder will find its place in the museum of theatrical props. Forever. The mountain will be reduced to rubble. We can be free of the misgovernment, lies and deceptions that are distorting our lives. For as long as we remain alive, we may dream and hope and act.

There is one other vista from my up along running that I have not shared until now. It was always a question of perspective, as to when I should run this past you, so to speak. Up above, the green stuff came more easily than it does now, down along. Especially on this gloomy and rain-soaked day. Think of it as a card up my sleeve, reserved for the more difficult times such as these.

One flourish of my magician's cloak and my ace is revealed. I turn my hand round and reveal my vision of hope, my inspiration. I see it every time I run down the hill if the weather is not too savage. And here, a perfect mirror image of this view, printed on the back of the playing card.

It is my lighthouse. The one I share with Virginia. Oh, Virginia! We are all in your debt, Mrs Woolf. In 1927, your classic novel *To the Lighthouse* saw the light of day and

Godrevy Island and its lighthouse, in the bay of St Ives,
photographed by Samuel Tan of Colour my Days

remains still one of the great works of English literature. It lay, like that, on the sea. With a dent in the middle and two sharp crags, and the sea swept in there and spread away for miles and miles. And there stood the lighthouse. A stark tower on a bare rock. Your words. Not mine. Yet seen through my eyes, too.

The grail in my running life. Virginia's lighthouse. The island and lighthouse of Godrevy in the bay of St Ives. I am a writer graced every run by knowing that out there, in the bay, is this symbol and reason for exploring my inner thoughts, wheresoever they take me. Catching my train to wisdom.

# 10

## THE GREAT CARBONA

Sweeping round to the left on the circuit road, the B3306, my running stride at last takes me past the entrance to Hellesveor farm, and I begin the descent of the Stennack hill, down towards the heart of St Ives and the sea. For a short while, there is no more paving, and my body is at the mercy of any car driver to my rear. If traffic appears on the other side of the road, cars behind me are forced to slow until I can mount the security of a pavement and they can accelerate past. Risks are all around us much of the time, but what bites deep into my psyche is the gratuitous peril so many are suffering in this pandemic.

The season of Advent is upon us. We are into December and Johnson and his ministers are celebrating the arrival of vaccines to protect us against the coronavirus. Oh my! How I rejoice in the wonder of science and the cleverness of the scientific community. But I am not doing so in the same spirit as these agents of our misgovernment. They are breathing a sigh of relief that their own skins may be saved. This tragedy for which they are responsible may be concluded more quickly and with a lower body count.

I make my microsecond judgements to ensure safe running as I enter this traffic junction. I am also entering my running "zone". The movement is becoming effortless. It is, above all, this awareness of the achievements of the scientific world that lifts my spirit and helps keep my running legs in motion. These last eight months have turned me into a fledgling scientist. And my contempt for politicians, who for reasons of greed and ambition have used and abused science and scientists, has deepened. "Following the science" has become a laughing stock expression. A travesty. A violation.

Time, I think, for another excursion into my magic tree to find myself a branch from which to play the prophet.

Our political leaders in the UK reek of incompetence. Theirs is a history of deadly ineptitude. Trust me, there will be cock-ups and grievous error in the roll-out of these vaccination programmes that we need so dearly. The bluster and rhetoric to which we have been subjected since this pandemic arrived will continue to be the order of the day. So many more people will die before their time.

Consider how much government failure there has been. No effective testing and tracing networks have ever been established, despite the opportunities provided by the first lockdown in the spring. The expertise of local authorities has been sidelined. Instead, those in government have opted to pay out huge sums to bring in private companies who may have had the connections to win the contracts but, too often, little or no experience and inadequate resources.

It could have been so different with a Corbyn-led, socialist government.

"Hey", some of you will be saying. "In your dreams. Call yourself an historian. You are writing romantic rubbish. Socialism never works. Corbyn was a disaster. Get real".

I stay with my claim. Our political and social and economic worlds could have been so much better for so many people if the Labour Party under Jeremy Corbyn had been voted into power in December last year and then started to honour its manifesto promises. When the clouds of coronavirus began to appear in February, do you think that Jeremy Corbyn would have made the same choices as Johnson and Cummings and followed the crazy and murderous path of achieving herd immunity without a vaccine? Or do you think he would have shared the same outlook as Jacinda Ardern in New Zealand and declared that such a course was "unthinkable"?

Of course, our path could have been like New Zealand's and our economy would now be prospering. The UK and New Zealand are both island nations. True, the Irish border is a complication for the UK, but New Zealand and the UK do not have the border issues facing so many European countries. Both countries would have had leaders with the political will to stop the advance of the pandemic. No doubt, there would have been problems. Other world leaders and the international media are shaped by the vested interests of the rich and powerful. Those benefiting from the unregulated excesses of capitalism for the last forty years and more have a lot to lose. They might have sought to tarnish British success. But the absence of body bags and a thriving economy would have spoken for themselves.

The dilemma for those who share my vision of the world is that those who do not have had their minds filled with the poisonous fruit of a small cluster of individuals who continue to control so much. Noam Chomsky, you remember, calls them the 0.1%. One person in a thousand. This is not wanton conspiracy theory. These guys are for real. They are the very few. But they are not immune from being outed and diminished.

How, then, can such hegemony over ideas and outlooks be broken?

The thoughts I share with you on this run of mine have always had that fundamental question in mind. I believe I have an answer. It holds together two approaches.

One is focused on the hope of a dawning awareness from below, from the millions and millions of people who are being abused and exploited in this country and elsewhere, that they are entitled to a better deal. That has always been tricky. Robert Tressell, the author of the classic socialist novel *The Ragged Trousered Philanthropists* (1914/1955), described with awesome clarity the failure of working men to identify the causes of their poverty in Edwardian England. I lament a similar blind spot within the masses of men and women who still tolerate their misgovernment at the hands of the likes of Johnson and Co.

The other is grappling with the complexities of creating a political party that can stand for those principles of justice and fairness that are embraced in the idea of socialism. A party that will fight in the interests of the many, naming and shaming the abusers and the exploiters, the malevolent and greedy few.

Could that be the Labour Party? Not, it seems, under Sir Keir Starmer. At the end of October, Jeremy Corbyn's membership of the Labour Party was suspended after he dared to comment on a report from the Equality and Human Rights Commission (EHRC) on anti-Semitism in the Labour Party under his leadership. When Corbyn's suspension was lifted in mid-November, the leader of the Opposition immediately withheld the Labour whip, leaving Jeremy Corbyn an independent MP. Starmer insisted he was doing this to show his zero-tolerance in tackling anti-Semitism.

I and others see this as a display of Starmer's intolerance of socialism and its threat to his own preferred policy of gaining the support of the masses and the Establishment. This Blairite, new Labour vision is one that will see us all crucified on the cross of global extinction, with billions of people sacrificed in the interests of human greed. That will not be Sir Keir Starmer's desire or intention. But it threatens to be the outcome of his refusal to embrace the spirit of socialism and his wilful attacks on those who do.

My feet have found the pavement again and I continue down the Stennack. A small cluster of cottages dating back to the 19th century is approaching on my left and the pavement outside their front doors narrows to a point where I must squeeze myself close to their front rooms as I pass. I dare not step out into the road. Ten seconds of peril, and then I am back to pavement with width and security. But now, on the other side of the road lies such a history that must have turned the world upside down at the time of its unfolding. I am drawn to it with a passion and a curiosity that reinvigorates me as a prophet. I will make the tale I now conjure as powerful as it deserves and needs to be. This is my home stretch. Running down the Stennack. I am on autopilot, and we are sharing magic bole time.

Do you recall my memory of how John and his friend

Jim had come over for coffee in the early days after we first arrived as Stennack residents? And how they could tell a tale or two? What follows is the full fruit of that morning when John and Jim shared their stories of the mines that lay beneath us, under the Stennack and its valley.

Here, with this name of "Stennack", we reach the heart of the matter. The steep incline that is called the Stennack runs from south-west to north-east down into St Ives. It takes its name from the river Stennack that flowed down this course, sometimes in full flood, and which, now, attentive pedestrians can hear under their feet or glimpse as a channelled stream by the roadside. The Stennack has been tamed but the name remains as a passport into one of the three livings for St Ives folk in the past. There was fishing, farming and – my focus – mining.

All this before the burgeoning of the tourism industry of today and the arrival of the "emmets", the sunburnt tourists. When the Romans came, not to holiday but to stay, in 43ad, they brought their language of Latin. The Latin name for tin is *stennum*, from which comes the chemical symbol for tin: Sn. Stennack means tinny. The river Stennack follows the line of one of the lodes of tin-bearing ore, cassiterite, that were formed around and within the granite masses some twenty million years after their initial raising.

Tin was first found on the surface in the river gravels, as it is now in Asia. When that has been exploited, you must go underground and mine for it, often under the copper-bearing lodes that penetrated the granite in these geological upheavals. We inhabit a landscape that still echoes to the sound of the thud of miners' boots, provided you have the ears to hear. Today, the price of tin may be rising, but eighty per cent of the world's supply comes from low-grade gravel deposits in Malaya, India and Thailand, and the exploitation of these reduced the price of mined Cornish tin in the 1980s and 1990s below the point of profitability. Cornish mining ended then, other than as a tourist exhibit.

But in and through the tales of men such as Jim and John, the soul of Cornish tin mining is glimpsed. The prize exhibit during their morning visit lay on our table. It was a survey plan of the lode that runs underground the length of the Stennack, showing where the main shafts are located that served the two main mines that worked this lode: St Ives Consolidated (known as Consols), towards the top of the incline, and Trenwith, lower down.

Our house rests between the western edge of the Trenwith mining area and the eastern edge of St Ives Consols. When we bought it, we had a mining search carried out and learnt that the available plans of the abandoned mines of St Ives Consols do not show the full extent of the underground workings. We do not have the full picture of all that human moles have carved under the surface of our neighbourhood. Less than two years ago, an old shaft opened in a small car park a couple of hundred yards distance from our home. Cornish shaft had revealed itself to the world again. This mine working was on an 1880s mine map. The estimate is that the shaft is several hundred feet deep, blocked at about forty feet by debris.

What became ever clearer listening to Jim and John was the sheer magnitude of the mining enterprise that had been a way of life for the best part of four generations of St Ives families – on and under the ground covered by the Stennack and its valley floodplain – from the early nineteenth century

The old mine shaft that opened near our house – image courtesy
of Toni Carver, editor of *The St Ives Times and Echo*

until the final closure of St Ives Consols in 1915.

John, the professional surveyor, was astounded at what
we were seeing in the map stretched out across our dinner
table. We were viewing a geological rarity: The Great Carbona
of the Stennack.

'Look! Can you see, running at right angles to the
direction of the lode. It extends for nine hundred feet and is
six hundred feet in depth and between fifty and seventy feet
wide! It's unlike anything else I've ever seen, and there are
smaller carbonas marked, too!'

I soon discovered that carbonas are large and unusual
ore formations, in this case of cassiterite, the tin-bearing ore,
which when excavated, produce large caverns whose roofs
had to be supported by massive timbers.

Let Cyril Noall, the St Ives historian of the last century,
explain what happened:

*In April 1843, a workman's lighted candle stuck against a beam in the fabulously rich "Great Carbona" and caused a disastrous fire which burned for six weeks and led to the destruction of that section of the mine.*

All gone. Four decades and more to excavate. And then, an industrial accident on such a scale that the Great Carbona ceases to exist.

For a moment, my focus returns to the Stennack of today. The community fire station is coming into view and, glancing sharp right, I can feel the damp and darkness of the mass of trees that borders the road. "Do not enter" is the message of the forbidding notice. Somewhere behind there, if I were to dig down in my imagination, I could find them. The blackened miners of St Ives from another age, fearing the worst, struggling to the surface, men choking and spitting as smoke filled their lungs. The flames curling up the wooden supports, swept higher by drafts of air as the temperature rose. By 1843, the cavern was huge, peppered with the timbers needed for propping up the roof towering above their heads. Still some tin left to mine but most now drilled out and raised to the surface, making James Halse, the owner, one of the richest men in the world.

They, my mining neighbours, remained trapped in their labour. Doomed to an early death. Hard men, placing their faith in each other and in a Wesleyan God. Or drink.

Now all gone, without trace.

Nothing of the Consols mine remains above ground. And who has heard of The Great Carbona? Yet, it would have deserved to be one of the wonders of its time. In a warped way. A geological rarity turned into a temple of Mammon

The site of The Great Carbona lies behind the community fire station
that I pass on my right, running down the Stennack

on the back of the sweat and muscle of Cornish labourers.
Men and women paid a pittance in proportion to the wealth
produced by their drills and picks and shovels.

I am playing with this imagery in the shade of the
branches of my magic tree. Is there a parallel to be found
here with a modern phenomenon? Can I mine a metaphor
to help my understanding of the predicaments we now face
in these pandemic times and their solutions? I hope you will
join me as I try.

# 11

## A CHRISTMAS EPIPHANY

The Christian festival of Epiphany is the annual celebration of the manifestation of the infant Jesus, the Christ child, to the Gentiles as represented by the Magi, the three wise men who appear in the story found in Matthew's gospel. This festival takes place on the sixth day of January, twelve days after Christmas. By association, an epiphany has come to mean a moment of sudden and great revelation. They are few and far between.

Will my search for a metaphor, inspired by the collapse of the Great Carbona, lead me to an epiphany moment? After all, this is a magic bole I am researching and thinking within. And how appropriate if such a wonder can be revealed in this chapter which records my thoughts in this Christmas season that ends with the festival of Epiphany. That designated time for celebrating the common humanity of our species. One saving message for all, Jew and Gentile alike.

What might such a metaphor need to explain? How would such a teasing out of meaning help us fashion a better world? Time, it seems, for some creative thinking.

Imagine we are in a fight for our very survival as a species.

Imagine that we can emerge triumphant from that battle and find we have created a just and more prosperous world with less inequality.

Imagine an economy where private enterprise and public investment combine to raise living standards for everyone.

Imagine a world where every rural and urban economy has sufficient health, education, and transportation services to meet the needs of local populations.

Imagine an economy where nations trade in ways that improve living standards and enhance environmental conditions for everyone.

Imagine a world where everyone can enjoy a carefree retirement, with all their food, housing, and healthcare needs met.

Imagine an economy where all manner of research is fully funded, with a steady stream of successful ideas commercialised or rolled out to serve the public.

Are you imagining? What an economy and world that would be!

Let me come clean. I share such a vision, but the words in this thought experiment belong largely to another. Time to introduce my American inspiration, Professor Stephanie Kelton. She is our leader in this exercise of imagination. This is part of her presentation in the book which has become an epiphany for me in the last two months of this pandemic year: *The Deficit Myth – Modern Monetary Theory and How to Build a Better Economy* (2020).

Ah! Economic theory! MMT! Alarm bells are sounding. As a prophet, I know when the message starts falling flat. The curious who gather at the edge of town to see and hear my outpourings begin to exchange glances of dismay. I sense the shuffling movements of discord within their midst. Towards the back of the crowd, I spot three or four slipping away to gather stones. I must take care. The prophet, if he is to prosper, needs to become a guide.

First, the metaphor.

The Great Carbona, sour fruit of 19th century capitalism, collapsed. I yearn to see the end of all monuments to Mammon, every man-made construction that serves as a tool for consolidating the riches of the overwealthy and powerful. And there is one edifice, above all, I have now in my sights, thanks to Stephanie Kelton. This construction, this way of thinking and acting, exists because nearly all governments have made similar uses of a flawed economic orthodoxy to manage their economies at our expense.

Thanks to our human capacity to think intelligently, we can hasten its demise. Right now. By embracing MMT. Modern Monetary Theory.

Now, let the tour begin.

I already had an outline grasp of MMT, but not by name. It had trickled through to my consciousness over this last decade. I understood that government finances should not be considered in the same way as ordinary household flows of income and expenditure. But it was not until reading Stephanie Kelton that I came to fully realise the strength of the MMT argument.

It is a worthwhile exercise to google "Modern Monetary Theory – a refutation" to find what a hornet's nest Kelton has disturbed. Orthodox economists really do not like having their ways of thinking upset. Behind the abstruse language that these male defenders of the status quo use, I sense panic. They assert their refutations with ferocity, but there is little intellectual engagement with the detailed and nuanced thrusts of her argument.

Cue Naomi Klein. I have referenced Professor Klein before in a magic tree moment on this run. Here she is again:

*In a world of epic, overlapping crises, Stephanie Kelton is an indispensable source of moral clarity... the truths that she teaches about money, debt, and deficits give us the tools we desperately need to build a safe future. Read it – then put it to use.*

Klein and Kelton. Clever women, with audacious and groundbreaking ideas. Threatening, perhaps, for many?

Stephanie Kelton's ideas have the power to set fire to a deeply flawed economics that has held us spellbound for decades. They reveal that the established ways of talking about what is politically possible, and our thinking about government spending, have been crackpot and at times, malevolent. An old economic and political paradigm could come crashing down. If enough people cotton on. And act.

A Copernican moment. The world really is as we never imagined it to be.

The US government issues its own currency: the dollar. The UK government issues its own currency: the pound sterling. MMT advocates are pointing out the simple truth that any government that issues its own currency can never run out of money. Economists and politicians and the media have, for whatever reasons, blinded themselves – and us – to this fact and all that follows from such a truth. We can build so much better an economy and society and world if we realise and act on this new understanding.

A week or so before Christmas this year, Rishi Sunak, the British chancellor, wrote an article in which he asserted that continuing to borrow billions of pounds – more than £300 billion extra in this year of the coronavirus pandemic – to meet public spending needs was wrong. "Morally, economically and politically". He repeated his promise to eliminate the "structural deficit".

Make no mistake, we are being set up for a return to austerity. And this at the same time as the United Nations' Children's Fund (UNICEF) announced on Thursday, 17 December 2020 that, for the first time in its seventy-year history, it will provide humanitarian aid to Britain's hungry children. After ten years of neoliberal austerity, we have come to this. One of the world's richest nations the recipient of UN aid.

The fact is that Sunak has got his economics hideously wrong. As have all his predecessors. How far through incompetence or malice remains open to further inquiry. But it is MMT that brings his grievous error to light, right now.

Note, MMT is not a religion, and it is not looking for disciples. What it offers is a realistic description of how a modern state currency, such as the dollar or the pound, works. It also offers some worthwhile ideas on how to transform that understanding into better public policy. And it helps us see more knowingly what the obstacles are – above all, inflation.

It also emphasises what the obstacles are not – our government will never run out of money. It is all smoke and mirrors when governments pretend that they cannot afford to borrow any more money or they cannot risk raising taxation. MMT opens the door to a new way of thinking about how we can run our economy.

Enough from my land of freethinking within my magic tree, at least for the time being. With Christmas almost here, I have around two hundred yards of my path home to complete. It is downhill motion still, with studied care not to trip passing the entrance and the exit to the carpark that now occupies the site of a garage, now long closed. Always the car, shaping this urban landscape. Add an "e" and make it feminine. Car becomes "care". Random thoughts still, but I am alive and there is joy in having a mind free to roam.

Where next? Back to the future with the prime minister of this weeping land. He is exercising great care, too. His concern is avoiding the blame for these pandemic deaths being laid at his door. To that end, the latest wheeze is proving remarkably successful.

On Saturday, 19 December, Johnson decided he had no option but to cancel Christmas for twenty-four million people in London and the south-east. It was another remarkable U-turn. For weeks, he and his ministers had been chorusing the message that three households could travel across the UK to mix in a Christmas bubble. Then came the realisation that hospitals within the NHS were on the point of breakdown such were the floods of patients being admitted with coronavirus infection. How could the government's carefully calibrated system of restrictions with its four tiers of severity not have worked?

The answer was found in a scientific report published by Public Health England, a government agency you may remember. A mutation had been found in the virus SARS-CoV-2 which was not more lethal nor was it able to defy the power of the new vaccines. But it was much more transmissible.

'Given the early evidence we have on this new variant of the virus and the potential risk it poses, it is with a very heavy heart I must tell you we cannot continue with Christmas as planned.' The leader's words. Vallance, his Chief Scientific Advisor, sounded almost Churchillian himself when he stood by Johnson and declared that, 'When the virus changes its method of attack, we as a country have to change our method of defence.' Grand words. Vallance acknowledged that the new variant of the virus had first been detected in September and by 9th December accounted for sixty-two per cent of all new cases in London. This mutation meant the virus was now up to seventy per cent more transmissible.

I began to smell bullshit. Yet again. I seem to have developed a nose for such odours during 2020. Do you recall my asking whether our leaders' amused contempt for the gullibility of the population at large had its own unique fragrance? True, I am speculating. I might be wrong. But I remain a doubting Thomas on this government-sanctioned reason why we have this Christmas emergency. Officially, it is all down to this mutation, this new strain of the virus: variant VUI-202012/01. But I think the reason for its rapid spread through southern England is due to the failure of the Government to limit the movement and mixing of the people. There has been no national lockdown. The government refused to impose higher tier restrictions in the south of the country as they had done in the north, where the spread of the virus then lessened for a while.

No matter that the UK New and Emerging Respiratory Virus Threats Advisory Group (NERVTAG) has now delivered its verdict that the new strain can spread more quickly. No matter that the World Health Organisation

(WHO) has been alerted. I am still picking up a foul odour. And it is emanating from an emperor wearing nothing. More research on my part, at the press of a button or two, led to the discovery that the WHO is, as one might expect, already on the case. On 22nd December, the WHO Working Group on COVID-19 Animal Models (WHO-COM) issued a statement about the UK and the South African SARS-CoV-2 new variants. The WHO-COM is an expert group of more than 150 scientists around the world with expertise in animal models of viral diseases. Their report acknowledges that epidemiological data suggests that these two variants may be associated with increased transmissibility. But it then goes on to say:

> *With respect to transmission studies, the group agreed that these* experiments [with laboratory animals] *are important but that they may be very difficult. Transmission studies give usually yes/no results with little room for comparison…* [Such research] *is a high operational priority.*

In short, there is no laboratory confirmation yet that this new variant is more transmissible. It could well be that the rapid increase in cases of coronavirus in southern England – as revealed in the epidemiological data (for instance, positive tests for infection and hospital admissions) – has occurred for another and obvious reason. People are spreading the disease to other people more and more because the restrictions on movement and space are not in place to stop them.

I had a History tutor at Catz, my Oxford college – Professor Peter Dickson – who taught me the meaning of the "post hoc, ergo propter hoc" fallacy. It has been a useful lesson, for life. Thank you, Peter. Translated from the Latin, the phrase reads "after this, therefore because of this". Because one event follows another, the former must have caused the latter. That is the fallacy. In this instance, the rapid increase in transmissions in southern England must have been caused by the new mutation in the coronavirus. Yet the true explanation for the phenomenon lies elsewhere: with the neoliberal Tory politicians who are blindly and stubbornly determined to prioritise the market rather than human life.

Suppose I am right, and this is a cunning deceit, what a wheeze this has turned out to be! In a matter of hours, this story has become the accepted explanation for the catastrophe unfolding around us. The mainstream media is following this narrative, without exception and without question. If there are scientists pointing to the lack of corroboration from within the WHO, their views are not being reported.

Interestingly, the immediate response of European leaders to these new COVID-19 mutation fears was to put Britain in quarantine. A total travel ban. Forty countries worldwide announced bans on flights. The thought did cross my mind that Europe has Johnson's card marked as a serial liar and deceiver. Always finding someone else to blame. So be it. Let him know we can use his latest audacious lie to our advantage, not least in the final stages of the Brexit negotiations that were concluded on Christmas Eve. Ten thousand angry lorry drivers from Europe, stranded outside Dover, became unfortunate short-term collateral in the bid to remind Johnson what a No Deal would look like.

Almost at the corner now. Passing the granite stone cottage on my left, so much older than the little boxes that have sprung up all around in the fields sold off by farmers struggling to make ends meet in times of agricultural depression. Granite is so hard. Yet elvan is reputed to be tougher. Elvan is the name used in Cornwall and Devon for the native varieties of quartz porphyry. It can be either white or blue. Blue elvan is also known as greenstone. Old men I have talked to say that when the miners met a piece of this quartz porphyry, they would turn the air blue with their curses. It was harder than granite. Out walking Ella, I once stumbled on a piece and suffered from fasciitis for six months. It even stopped me running.

Enough. I am running now, rounding the corner. Only a few yards from the steps to the front door and home. The change of gradient from down to uphill begins to drain what is left of my energy and I must dig in hard for these last strides. There! My hand closes in on the granite stone in the corner of the small front garden that lies at my shoulder height. I always perform this ritual clutching of the rock on returning home from a local circuit run, before mounting the steps to reach the front door. The steps I fell headfirst down back in March.

Still playing with ideas and memories gathered over a lifetime.

"One step backwards, two steps forwards".

The thoughts of chairman Mao, fruits of the Long March.

We are on our own Long March, but our leader is no Mao.

Let me leave you with the message of hope that Modern Monetary Theory inspires in me. Remember, MMT is not a religion, and I am not in the conversion business. But I cannot free myself from being still the person who has spent a working lifetime as a teacher, as well as an academic, and nor do I want to. I will, though, leave you to find out more for yourself about this new way of thinking about the economy and politics – with just a few tasters I cannot resist:

Myths and misunderstandings about money, debt, and taxes are embedded in our culture and in our heads. By dissolving these misapprehensions, it becomes possible to build a better future.

MMT describes the real world where the government spends first and then taxes or borrows afterwards. Here in the UK, Chancellor Sunak ordered buttons to be pushed to create the billions of pounds of support in this pandemic crisis. He was not waiting on our taxes or loan advances from financiers before doing so.

In fact, our taxes do not actually pay for anything, at least not at the level of central government in the UK nor at the federal level in the US. The government does not need our money. We need their money. We have got the whole thing backwards!

In 1971, President Richard Nixon ended the US link to the gold standard, where the dollar was pegged to the value of gold, and all other currencies then pegged to the value of the US dollar. From that act of state, a new range of possibilities opened. But much of our economic and political conversation is still rooted in an outmoded, pre-1971 way of thinking.

It is no longer appropriate to ask: "where's the money coming from?". And that has been the case for fifty years. Sometimes, we can be such dinosaurs.

If like me, you have had no formal training in economics, there will be parts of Professor Kelton's argument that will be difficult to follow. But the overall thrust of her insights and the basic argument that underpins them are clear enough. And we can all share the exhilaration she felt when the penny dropped.

Oh! How I would love the Great Carbona of unregulated capitalism to catch fire and burn and collapse into dust, as my local carbona did in 1842. If enough people cotton on to the ways we are being hoodwinked, it will.

I will leave the last words for Bernie Sanders, the American socialist and presidential candidate:

"Change always comes from the bottom up".

# 12

## THE YEAR AHEAD

Warming down.
       Resting on the bed.
  Stretched out.
  Stretchered off.
  Laid out.
  Dead.

Free association time. The wordsmith awakens. There is a poet in me, slumbering.

This book of mine, for such it has become, records the thoughts that have bubbled to the surface through the complex circuits of my mind during these ten months of pandemic awareness. My thoughts and the results of my research, for I am a historian who has also become a fledgling scientist and a trainee economist.

It seems to me you need to have a variety of personae if you are to survive a pandemic and bear fruit. You also need a bit of luck. But I have always been a magician, conjuring into life my own good fortune. With the help of my guardian angels, of course. They deserve their own special billing.

I have never told you this story before. I was rushing to catch the last train back home one summer's evening in Ipswich in Suffolk. The year was 1996. My head was filled with thoughts sparked by the seminar I had been attending. And I failed to remember the golden rule. We all need to look right and then left and then right again, crossing roads. Especially runners! As I moved smoothly off the pavement onto the thoroughfare, my guardian angels exchanged a nanosecond glance and decided. At that exact moment, the angel on my right shoulder slammed on my running brakes, and I froze, stock-still, feet away from the kerb.

The look of horror on the face of the young girl sitting in the car's nearside back passenger seat I can still see, her eyes glazed over in anticipation. An imagined road traffic accident where a vehicle decelerating from over 40mph hits unprotected human flesh at around 35mph. That freeze-frame moment was all I recall as the vehicle swept past me.

If the car had hit me then, I most likely would have died. A waste, but accidents happen. I had become careless and so opened the door to my doom. Even so, my guardian angels chose to intervene. You could say they were only doing their job. However, even angels employed as personal protection equipment do reach their expiry date. Yet this, they must have decided, was neither their exit moment nor mine.

Flight now became the order of the evening. And I had a train to catch. I sprinted away from the scene. By the skin of my teeth, as the saying goes, I did find myself sitting in a carriage on that train, my heart still beating fast, counting my blessings.

By accelerating away, I managed to avoid any inquiry into

my careless stupidity running wild through urban streets. Will those who have been misgoverning us escape, too? Will they dodge a formal examination of the outcomes of their recklessness? My folly had not led to any loss of life. No one had been harmed. But these Tory donkeys have led us into a slaughterhouse where the numbers of excess deaths in the UK now matches the worst years in WWII. COVID-19-related deaths are expected to exceed one hundred thousand by the end of this third week in January, according to the Office for National Statistics. Even on the significantly lower official death toll of around eighty-three thousand published by the government, which counts only people who have died within twenty-eight days of a positive test, the UK has more deaths per one million population than any other country in the world, other than Italy.

Oh my! We are such a world-beating nation! And if we are to meet the government's goal, a pledge from the prime minister no less, of immunising by the middle of February all 14.6 million people in the top four at-risk groups – the over seventies (which includes me!), NHS and social care workers, care home residents and the extremely clinically vulnerable – there will need to be around 350,000 vaccinations a day. We have a long way to go to reach that kind of outcome.

Such a catalogue it has been, this detailing of the consequences of the madness and badness of Johnson and Cummings over most of these past ten months. Maybe for all those months. Who knows what goes on behind the doors of government during a pandemic? The mainstream media still reveals little, although a few journalists are now allowed to indulge their rants about how awful this way of governing has turned out to be. Perhaps Johnson and Cummings are still in conference, stirring their cauldron of spells, brought together by Zoom.

I know I have become weary as these months of mayhem pass. Yet, very many of our population will be more exhausted than me. They are living closer to infection, although even Cornwall is catching up fast in the table of risk. And when people feel the tide is turning against them, they look for comfort and security. They need to believe that their government can and will take the necessary actions to bring matters under control. They do not want to hear that their leaders view ordinary people with disdain and are quite prepared to sacrifice them on the altar of their own economic ideology. That is one reason why Johnson and his party are not being savaged by angry men and women in revolt.

There I go again. My anger getting the better of me. Rage is best exercised with a modicum of control. This, after all, is my warm-down time. A chance to relax. An opportunity to allow the endorphins to speed through my body and fill me with contentment. That is what happens after a run. It is the natural order of the world.

But this world has been turned upside down. Do you remember, back in the spring, the prophetic words that surfaced on my run uphill?

*The old world dies and in the new world we have no option other than to keep going.*

*The bubble of disease has settled on us and clicked tight.*

True, we still have hope. We all cling to that gift from Pandora's box. But when I look to the coming months in this new year, 2021, I know that still more human lives will be cut short in unnatural deaths. There has never been, during this plague, so many people dying as now. Those infected during

December last year, when we should have had the tightest of restrictions and did not, are dying now in January, four to five weeks later. Between two and three per cent of those infected die. That is the inescapable statistic. The critical fact you hardly ever hear in the mainstream media. And so, it will go on.

Remember the borough of Brent in north London in the first wave and who died? Most of those who are dying now will be BAME groups. Not those of White ethnicity.

Many of those who died in the spring were residents of care homes for the elderly. That was true in Brent, too. We know the order came to release the elderly, untested for COVID-19 infection, from hospital back into care homes.

Why?

To free the beds for the waves of new coronavirus cases.

Who was responsible?

Who gave that unthinkable order?

Yes, the anger still throbs. For ten months, I have been compiling this dossier of deceits and lies, detailing incompetency and exposing the contempt this apology of a UK government shows for those in the lower ranks of their make-believe "natural hierarchy". Johnson and Cummings share more than a university education at Oxford. They are both on record as believers in the primary role of genes in shaping so-called IQ. Cummings even went so far in a 2014 blog post to suggest that it was a good idea to develop "designer babies" and that IQ could be predicted by genetic analysis. Furthermore, the NHS should be funded so everybody could design their own babies to avoid an unfair advantage for the wealthy. How cunning a twist to conceal the malice behind the ideas!

Such bad science.

What appalling morality.

How implausible and sick the speculation.

Do you recall my presentation of Dominic Cummings as the advocate of herd immunity in February 2020?

"At a private engagement at the end of February, Cummings outlined the government's strategy. Those present say it was herd immunity, protect the economy, and if that means some pensioners die, too bad."

Louise, my therapist-wife, suggests it would be useful to know whether either Johnson or Cummings ever had the gift of a teddy bear in their early childhood. And if they did, how long was it before they destroyed those wretched transitional objects?

When I was a child, I had my Peter Ted. I still do. Give me a child until he is seven and I will give you the man. That is the old Jesuit belief. I believe there is much truth in it. Johnson and Cummings can always plead their first seven years to explain their status as emotional cripples in adult life.

Michael Apted, the film director who died at the beginning of this new year aged seventy-nine, took this wisdom and made it the foundation for a TV series that lasted his lifetime. In 1964, he worked as a researcher for *7 Up*, a programme that featured children from backgrounds divided by class and wealth. And then, every seven years, he returned as the director to film them as they grew older. What genius! How remarkable the looking glass he created for us to examine others of our humankind making their journey from cradle to grave. It was my privilege as a teacher to share these programmes with thousands and thousands of my students. My gift to them. I doubt whether the national inspectorate, the Office for Standards in Education (OFSTED), would have been happy if they had known. Not enough intervention from me. Lacking specific goals and learning outcomes.

We need, so much, to find or be given the time to reflect upon ourselves. To consider how we have come to be who we are. I fell in love with history because I wanted to fathom my own past. Know thyself. The Socratic wisdom. Only when you have begun to chart the depths of your own being can you begin to understand others. Empathy, that outreaching to others of our humankind, cannot grow in those who are scared to reach for the mirror.

Erich Fromm, the psychoanalyst, understood and communicated this truth in *The Art of Loving* (1956). "Loving" is an art that requires learning. It is a wisdom that needs work to achieve. When we focus on this art of loving, we satisfy the deepest drives of humanity: the need to overcome separateness; the need to find atonement. All ages and all cultures face the same needs.

Unfortunately, the PM of the UK neither knows nor loves himself. He acts to maximise his own interests, but that is not the authentic self-love that Professor Fromm advocates. Unless you know how to love yourself, you cannot love other people. One hundred thousand UK citizens, and still counting, have died due to the actions and inactions of two sad men, Johnson and Cummings, and the men and women who have thrown in their lot with them. All of them, if examined, will fail Fromm's criterion for being able to love well:

*…the main condition for the achievement of love is the* overcoming *of one's* narcissism.

No one should die and be dismissed Cummings-style with perfunctory dispatch:

"Too bad".

"Too bad".

"Too bad".

But for Cummings and Johnson, they were, after all, only collateral damage in the grand project. Managing a pandemic.

"We are, do not forget, your natural leaders. The brightest and the best. We made our mark with Get Brexit Done. Now, stand and raise your glasses in celebration of our follow-up: 'Getting Away with Murder'."

Such a slaughter of innocents. These pages should be soaked in tears for all these people whose lives have been cut short.

Lying here on our bed, another memory from childhood breaks the surface of my thoughts. My mum, at times, would look at me with wonder and muse:

'You never stopped crying as a baby.'

Well, there you go. That I do not remember. But there did come a time when I was old enough to shed tears and sob uncontrollably and remember doing so.

I must have been nearly five years old. I was a slow learner, but I did understand about birds and nests and flying. We lived in a newly built semi-detached house with a back garden in which there was a garden shed. My mum was the gardener, not my dad. That spring, a bird made the wrong decision and made its nest in that shed. I think I was the one who made the discovery. Not yet at school and exploring my world. I even knew enough to be able to name the bird. It was a robin. I did not yet know enough to understand that it takes two robins to make a nest and create the eggs.

'You shouldn't have left the window open, Rosie.' My father to my mum.

'Well, I wasn't to know, was I?' My mum, defensively.

'We can't have birds taking over our shed. What do you think Mr Baines next door will say?' My father, more heatedly.

He strode into my imagination, wrenching the nest from its crafted location and then emerging triumphant, clutching their home.

'This is for the bin! Shut the bloody window. And do something about Robert.'

At that point, I began to wail, not just sob. I could see my robin flying free, out of the shed and away, over my father's head. I was too young to know, but my robin needed to escape. Birds tell such powerful stories if we care to listen. The robin has appeared several times in my life. As has the cuckoo. And the swallow.

Back to my dad. Still very much there. He could be a kind man, my dad. But for him, having your father disappear as soon as you come into the world in a strange city, that must have been hard. He was the child of emigrants to the USA, newly resident in New York. An Irish father and an English mother. When Patrick abandoned her, his mum needed an assisted passage back across the Atlantic to England in 1908, clutching her tearful baby.

My father must have had his guardian angels, too. His life was never cut short. He lived, as did my mum, to the ripe old age of eighty-four. Meaning he survived not only the ordinary pitfalls of human existence but the killing fields of the Spanish flu and WWII.

It says a lot that my memory of him has risen through the filters like this. If you have a father around, it is natural to begin life needing him to be perfect. And then, just as natural to grow older learning to come to terms with his failure to match those dreams. My dad, of course, never had those experiences. He had no father figure, as far as I know. His mum was out charring all day. It was his grandmother who reared him. Making sense of all that must have been difficult.

There is a photo of my father that eventually found its way into my collection. It is undated, but he once talked about it. He is the one in the brown shirt. Mother and Grandmother could not afford a white shirt. The male teacher had survived the trenches and was harsh and strange. The year was 1919 or 1920. For me, this image is so important. It captures perfectly why I made my meaning in the classroom for three decades of my life, struggling to resist this style of education. But beyond that, there is much that the picture does not yield. You have no inkling that the world is losing between 2.5 and 5 per cent of its humankind in the viral pandemic of the

My dad, Frank Donovan, in the brown shirt, is participating in a drill exercise at his council school in Sidcup, Kent, circa 1919

Spanish flu. And I will never know what was going on in my father's head as the camera clicked. Is he laughing? Or is that the look of a boy terrified he will be caught doing something wrong?

Across the world now, as this pandemic rages ever more fiercely, there are billions of people looking with longing to their father figures for guidance and love and meaning in the fantasy land of politics and government. There are Americans in love with Trump, Chinese adoring Xi Jinping, Indians revering Modi, Brazilians who worship Bolsonaro. My God, there are even Brits who still think the sun shines out of Johnson's rear end.

Poor, deluded masses,

Please,

Please,

Please,

Learn to fly.

# Acknowledgements

I would like to thank all those private individuals – Robin, John, David, Ben and Tanya – whose names appear in this work and who have confirmed that I may reference them and that they are in favour of publication. As for the public individuals whose names keep cropping up in my chapters, I remain free to comment on their political and social actions and draw conclusions about their character.

My debt to three special people is considerable. I am so grateful to Jessica Raber in the USA and to Ingrid Helmer in the Netherlands for being my literary guides. They have read and critiqued each chapter as I wrote, saving me from my clumsiness on shall we say more than one occasion. I also extend my deep gratitude to Howard Pue, the father of Jessica Raber, who has been my main guide in understanding the science of this coronavirus pandemic. My debt to Laura Spinney, the author of *Pale Rider* (2017), for her account of the Spanish flu pandemic, is acknowledged in chapter 6.

Seven of the twenty-two images that appear in these pages are not from my camera or from my family albums. I acknowledge here, with much thanks, the permissions that I have been granted for the use of these images:

Cornish tin miners taken by J.C.Burrows in 1894 – permission granted by the Royal Cornwall Museum, Truro and a licence purchased for its use at sales@mediastorehouse. com.

Daily COVID-19 Deaths/Millions – 3rd June 2020 – permission granted by The John Hopkins University in the USA.

Global Extinction demonstration outside the Royal Cornwall Hospital, Truro – permissions granted by the photojournalist James Pearce at http://www.lexisplace. co.uk and a donation made.

Image of the SARS-CoV-2 virus by Radoslav Zilinsky – 1212213050 – permission granted by Getty Images and a licence purchased.

Godrevy island and lighthouse, in the bay of St Ives – permission granted by Samuel Tan of Colour my Days at https://www.colourmydays.com and a donation made.

The old mine shaft that opened up in a carpark near our house – permission granted by Toni Carver, editor of our excellent local newspaper: the *St Ives Times and Echo*.

Finally, and very importantly, I acknowledge the special debt I owe my wife, Louise, my *sine qua non*.